Simon Peter
and the
King

Simon Peter
and the
King

Rhonda Calhoun

HEART
PUBLISHING

Simon Peter and the King
by Rhonda Calhoun

Other books by Rhonda Calhoun:
THE BRIDE
BLESSED ARE THE POOR
SIMON PETER AND THE MASTER

Heart Publishing
12905 South 71 Hwy. #177
Grandview, MO 64030
harvesthome@juno.com
www.harvesthome.org
816-522-9011

Printed in the United States of America
International Standard Book Number: 0-9719140-3-6

Special thanks to:
Cover design by Dan Arnold
www.imdarnold@comcast.net

Illustration by Pam Macchi
copyright © 2005 HEART PUBLISHING
All rights reserved

Edited by Edie Veach
ironsharp@flmtgif.org

This book is dedicated to
the King of glory who rescued me
from a deep, dark pit and set me on the Rock.
This perfect, beautiful Man
has loved me even in my weakness,
And He has loved me well.

TABLE OF CONTENTS

FOREWORD

The prequel to this book you hold in your hands, *Simon Peter and the Master*, began with the Apostle Peter in the depths of Nero's dungeon, declaring the excellent testimony of his Savior, the Man Christ Jesus. Now, in *Simon Peter and the King*, Peter proclaims Christ's Lordship as he bears witness to the One, True and Faithful Sovereign Lord over all.

The depiction of Simon Peter's life within these pages magnifies the glorious rewards of following Christ with wholehearted affection. Captivated by his King, Peter endures hardship like a good soldier, seeking to obtain the outcome of his faith—the very salvation of his soul—while casting his net for the souls of men.

I recommend this sequel from Rhonda Calhoun. Having worked with her from 1995, I can tell you that she, like Peter, serves her King with genuine devotion as she lays down her life for Him. Such extravagant worship flows from her as she sacrificially serves men, women and children in need—those oft overlooked by the masses.

Once again, I am confident that your heart and life will

be impacted by *Simon Peter and the King.* This book is filled with truth and mercy and love—a love that never fails to overwhelmingly effect and change those who receive it, even those in Nero's dungeon.

Mike Bickle
Director,
International House of Prayer of Kansas City

AUTHOR'S NOTE

My writing of *Simon Peter and the Master,* which is the first book of the *Simon Peter* series came about as a result of a dream. In this dream, I listened as Peter sat chained in a dungeon sharing the gospel with his fellow prisoners. As I was waking up, I thought to myself, "This would make a good book." I heard someone answer, "It certainly would." At that moment, I knew that I was to write a book about Peter's time in prison, but I had no idea what that involved.

I began to research Peter's life and discovered that he spent the last nine months of his life in Nero's dungeon, a fact of which I had no idea. Encouraged, I wrote the first chapter, which was based on my dream. As the book began to take shape and grow, I realized that the book was going to be too large for just one volume and the Simon Peter series was born.

During the writing of the second book, *Simon Peter and the King,* the Lord spoke to my heart asking me why I was writing these books. I learned a long time ago that Jesus does not ask a question in order to gain information. So, I asked Him to tell me. He answered, "To help prepare My church for persecution and martyrdom."

I must admit that this was not something that I had thought of or ever aspired to do. After all, we live in a nation known for its religious freedom and perecution and martyrdom is not something most of us ever think about. But, I could not deny what I had heard.

Just as I did in *Simon Peter and the Master,* I have presented the gospel events in the order of their occurrence rather than the order they are presented in the New Testament, which gives a greater understanding of the day-to-day interaction Jesus had with both His disciples and the people of the land. In the few instances where it is not quite clear when or where a particular event happened, I placed the event in the story when or where it seemed to most likely have occurred.

I have diligently sought to portray each event in the same manner it is related in the Scriptures. In some instances, I have included additional dialogues to help further explain the subject being discussed. I have also included various commentaries and references concerning the Jewish customs of the day, which further helps bring the Scriptures to light.

My desire is that your heart will be captured by the beauty and kindness of the King as you read this book. I pray that your heart will grow more in love with our beloved Savior, for a heart in love is more likely to remain true in an hour of testing than a lukewarm, indifferent one.

For His Glory,
Rhonda

Who do you say that I am?

Lift up your heads, O gates,
and be lifted up, O ancient doors,
that the King of glory may come in!

Who is the King of glory?
The LORD strong and mighty,
The LORD mighty in battle.

Lift up your heads, O gates,
and lift them up, O ancient doors,
that the King of glory may come in!

Who is this King of glory?
The LORD of hosts, He is the King of glory.

Psalm 24:7-10

CHAPTER ONE

The prison door opens, and Brutus storms in shouting, "What are you so happy about?"

I respond by silently crying out to the One who sees every bird that falls to the ground and counts every hair on my head.

"Haven't you had enough, Christian? Don't you realize that your so called Messiah doesn't care about you? Don't you know that he is dead and absolutely powerless against the likes of me?"

"I know that my Redeemer lives and is sitting on a throne beside His Father interceding for me right now," I answer as supernatural grace and strength pours through me.

Kicking me in the backside, Brutus shouts, "Your so called redeemer died on a cross over thirty years ago, you foolish old man!"

"You are right, Brutus. Jesus did die, but three days later He rose again. Several days after His resurrection, I saw Him with my very own eyes, and I even talked with Him. I touched Him, and I can tell you that He was very

1

much alive."

"Once dead, always dead, I say. Speaking of death, your execution draws nigh, and then you will find yourself in the same condition as your dead Messiah."

"Brutus, it would be to your best interest to consider the fact that, if I am right and Jesus is indeed the Son of God, then you are in serious trouble. Don't you think it would be wise for you to at least consider the possibility that what I say is true? Stop and think, Brutus, what do I have to gain by proclaiming that Jesus is the Son of God?"

"Others have died for lesser causes," Brutus answers.

"That is true, but what man has ever given his life for something that he knew to be a lie? Do you not realize that I would never have endured such devastating atrocities as I have suffered if I was not absolutely, without a shadow of a doubt, certain that Jesus is indeed the Son of God who can take away the sins of the world, which includes yours, my friend?"

For the first time, Brutus has no response.

Father, open his eyes that he might see and know the truth, I pray.

I continue, "Brutus, Jesus is indeed the Son of God, and He did die, and He rose again so that men like you and me can have our sins washed away and enter His eternal Kingdom."

"Shut-up! Just shut-up! I don't want to hear anymore of your bewitching words!" he shouts as he storms out of our cell, slamming the door behind him.

Cursing loudly, he drops his keys only to storm off commanding another guard to lock the door.

"I guess truth is painful," Justus says.

"Especially when you don't want to hear it," I add.

"Peter, your patience and kindness towards Brutus are remarkable," Josiah says.

"It is only because of the Lord that I am able to love

that man. Believe me, there are times when I find myself slipping back into my old ways, but the Lord is faithful to convict me. He is faithful to keep me."

Feeling quite ill from the infection that has consumed my broken leg, I lean my head back against the stone wall and try to focus on the possibility that Malchus might be bringing my wife to see me today.

Lord, would You make a way for Malchus? Would You clear a path and bring my wife to me? I would so love to see her again.

I soon fall into a fitful sleep only to wake to the sound of moaning. Eleazer is in agony because of the whipping he took earlier at the hands of Brutus. I hear Justus, Josiah and Laban fervently praying for him.

I am so thankful for my friends, and I am also thankful that I am no longer chained, Lord.

"Eleazer, my brother, I am coming to pray for you," I speak into the darkness as I drag my broken leg behind me. The pain is excruciating; it is almost more than I can bear.

Lord, give me the strength I need, I pray.

Eleazer responds, "Why bother? If your God does not heal faithful servants like you, then why should he intervene for someone who does not even believe that he exists?"

"God is kind to both evil and good men, to the righteous and the unrighteous. And God always answers our prayers, but sometimes His answer seems to delay, and often the answer looks different from what we expected. Eleazer, now is the time to reach out and take His hand, for He will take you up. He is a strong tower; He is your refuge. Underneath the shadow of His wings is a hiding place, a shelter from the storm and a respite from the pain," I respond.[1]

"I cannot do as you say because I do not believe you,"

he replies.

"Well, I believe therefore I will pray," I answer as I lay my hands on his shoulder. Wet, sticky blood has thoroughly soaked his garment.

Brutus's whip did more damage than I realized.

I whisper, "In the name of Jesus Christ, be healed, my friend and brother."

I wait. Eleazer is motionless.

Oh divine Master, would You do what only You can do? Send Your healing power, I pray.

Eleazer clears his throat.

"Oh great Physician, come and heal just as You did while on earth," I pray.

"Peter, something is happening! Something is definitely happening!" Eleazer exclaims.

"What is it?" Laban excitedly asks.

"I can hardly believe it—the searing pain has gone!" he exclaims. His voice is filled with awe.

I run my hand over his shoulder and down his back. His garment is no longer wet. "Is there any pain at all?" I ask.

He answers, "Absolutely none."

"Eleazer, you have just been healed by the Master's hand!" I exclaim as joy floods my being.

"I knew it!" Josiah nearly shouts, "I knew Jesus would heal him!"

"Oh, how wonderful! Oh, how glorious of the King!" Laban adds.

"Now, will you believe, Eleazer? Will you surrender your life to Jesus?" Justus excitedly asks.

"The fact that something has happened I cannot deny, but that does not necessarily prove your case. I must think on these things. I must ponder them," Eleazer says, his voice fades away like a leaf floating downstream.

"But," Josiah exclaims, quickly lowering his voice, "how

can you have any doubt? Jesus just healed you! That is called a miracle where I come from! Surely, you do not think there is any other explanation?"

"I admit that I cannot explain how this has happened, but I will not embrace Peter's doctrine based solely on a single event. I need more evidence," he answers.

Father, would You remove the scales from his eyes just as You did for Saul on the road to Damascus?

"Eleazer, the Lord desires to save you from eternal destruction and grant you entrance into His eternal Kingdom. Therefore, I will continue to pray that He will draw you into His heart, into His marvelous love," I say.

I move away so that I can prop against the stone wall in an effort to find some relief for my very painful leg. I am sweating profusely because of the pain and the fever.

Justus asks, "Peter, what about your wounds?"

"I am in great agony, my friend. Would you pray for me to be healed?" I ask.

Thoroughly exhausted, I decide to lie down. The stones are cold, damp and filthy. I can feel insects crawling on the open wounds on my back, chest and broken leg.

Probably maggots. I hate maggots, always have.

"Me? I cannot pray for healing!" Justus responds.

"Yes you can. It is not the man who does the healing; it is the Lord," I answer.

"But, Peter, I do not know how!"

"You do not have to know how, my friend. Simply fix your eyes on Jesus, the author and perfecter of your faith, who for the joy set before Him, which was you and I, endured the cross and now sits at the right hand of the throne of God. Set your gaze on Him and simply ask for His help."[2]

"But, I really don't know how," he responds.

"All you have to do is ask," I say, my teeth chattering as cold chills rack my body and sweat pours down my face and neck.

"Justus, I will pray with you," Josiah adds.

"I will do as you have asked not because of any confidence in myself but merely because I care about you," Justus answers. After a long silence, he timidly prays, "God, will You come and heal Peter?"

Josiah whispers, "In the name of Jesus Christ, be healed, my friend and brother!"

I wait expectantly, but nothing happens.

Laban adds, "Jesus, I know that You love Peter, and I know that You love me, even though I do not deserve it. Based on the fact that You are good, would You look down upon Your servant and Your friend and heal his body, we all pray."

Like warm, soothing oil, the wonderful presence of God thoroughly covers me. I bask in His glorious presence.

Oh, my Beloved King, how wonderful You are!

The pain and fever are still with me, but I barely notice, for my inner man is being strengthened.

You are here, and You love me! I can feel Your great heart for me and I adore You! You are better than life, better than anything!

"Peter, what is this that I feel?" Laban asks, whispering.

Before I can answer, Josiah says, "Whatever this is, I like it!"

"Me, too," Justus adds.

"This is the incredible, intoxicating presence of God," I answer.

"Has He healed you?" Justus asks.

"Not yet, but I trust Him. He always does everything just right and in His perfect time," I answer. I then turn my attention to my Jewish brother, saying, "Eleazer, Jesus is manifesting His presence in this dark prison. I am keenly aware of His presence as are Josiah, Laban and Justus. He's here and wants us to know it. He longs to bring you into His Kingdom! Reach out your hand, my friend, and allow Him to touch more than your physical body, allow Him to touch your heart that you might believe."

"I will not do such a foolish thing," Eleazer responds.

"God uses the foolish things of this world to shame the wise, and God has chosen the weak things of the world to shame the things which are strong. He chooses the base things of the world and the despised so that no man should boast before Him. So, dare to be foolish for once in your life and open your heart to Jesus, my friend. Believe me, you won't regret it."[3]

"I cannot do what you ask. I still have too many unanswered questions. There are too many things that you have said that do not make sense to me," he responds.

"Now I know why God chose me," Josiah says chuckling. "It is because I am foolish."

"I may be foolish, but that's okay with me because one minute in His presence is worth it! I've never felt anything that even comes close to this," Laban exclaims.

"I agree," Justus says.

Jesus, You kissed a guilty world with Your mercy and love! I stand in awe of You, my Beloved Savior and Friend! Thank You for manifesting Your presence to us this day!

Eleazer says, "Peter, I would like to believe that what you say is true, but I cannot reconcile all that I know with all that you say."

I respond, "A natural man does not accept the things of the Spirit of God; for they are foolishness to him. You cannot fully understand God with your natural mind, my friend. He is so far beyond your natural ability to understand. God is love, and who can understand love? Love is like the wind—you cannot contain it and neither can you see it. The wind blows where it wishes, and you hear the sound of it but do not know where it comes from or where it is going; so is everyone who is born of the

Spirit."[4]

The weighty, exhilarating presence of God gently begins to lift.

Oh, please do not go! Not yet! Just one more minute, I pray!

I lay on the cold, filthy stone floor searching the thick darkness for any sign of His presence. I can no longer feel Him, but I know that He is still here; He is always here, for His Spirit lives within me, and He ever intercedes for me.[5]

With the Lord's manifest presence gone, I become painfully aware of my physical body again.

Kind Father, would You give me the strength to rejoice and be glad, for I am persecuted and in great agony? [6] And Father, would You make a way for my beloved wife to visit me?

Eleazer interrupts my thoughts by saying, "Peter, why would your God heal me and not heal you?"

"God's ways are perfect and often make no sense. In times like these, one must trust that God knows best and has our best interest at heart at all times and in every situation. Being a Christian means trusting the One who gave His life for you with your past, your present and your future."

"I do not understand why God would heal me and not you; it makes no sense at all. You would think that he would heal his followers rather than one who questions his very existence," Eleazer says.

"Perhaps, He was trying to get your attention? Perhaps, He was demonstrating to you that He is good and kind and loving? Perhaps, He was showing you that He sees you and cares?"

"Perhaps." Eleazer responds.

Eleazer grows quiet, and I silently pray.

Josiah asks, "Peter, I know that you are in pain, so if it is too much to ask just tell me so, but are you able to tell us more about the One you call Master?"

"As the Lord gives me grace, I will do so, my brother."

CHAPTER TWO

As Jesus made His way through the busy streets of Capernaum, more and more people gathered to Him. I had come to realize that the majority of people did not follow the Master because they believed that He was the Messiah, but most followed because they were eager to see the miracles that He performed.

It had also become very evident to me that His steps were ordered by God. Nothing Jesus did was by chance. On the contrary, He knew exactly what He was doing and where He was going at all times. It seemed as though He had a script for each event, and He faithfully and carefully fulfilled every detail of it.

My thoughts were interrupted as Jesus came to a sudden stop. He was looking at a house. The front door was open, which in the Jewish culture was an invitation for anyone who so desired to enter.

The Master led us inside where we were warmly welcomed by an elderly man who introduced himself as Jacob. The crowd followed, filling the house until there was standing room only at which point Jesus quieted the crowd. Taking a seat, He taught and cast out devils.

Several Scribes and Pharisees pushed their way through the crowd eager to be front and center. Jesus seemed oblivious to their approach. The eldest among the men, with his arms folded tightly across his chest, cleared his throat and said, "Teacher, we want to see a sign from you."

They are testing Him! They are trying to trap Him!

For a moment, everyone grew silent.

"Yeah, we want to see a sign," a man from the crowd yelled out.

A voice from the back of the room shouted, "Jesus casts out demons by Beelzebub, the ruler of the demons!" This created an immediate response from the crowd, some positive and some negative.

The Pharisees and Scribes looked at each other with a smug look.

They think they have Him.

Raising His hand, Jesus quieted the people and responded, "Any kingdom divided against itself is laid waste; and a house divided against itself falls. If Satan is divided against himself, how shall his kingdom stand? You say that I cast out demons by Beelzebub. If I by Beelzebub cast out demons, by whom do your sons cast them out?"

No one answered a word.

Jesus continued, "Consequently they shall be your judges. But if I cast out demons by the finger of God, then the Kingdom of God has come upon you."

Turning to Jacob, Jesus said, "When a strong man, fully armed, guards his own homestead, his possessions are undisturbed; but when someone stronger than he attacks him and overpowers him, he takes away from him all his armor on which he had relied, and distributes his plunder."

Laying His hand on Jacob's shoulder, He continued, "He who is not with Me is against Me; and he who does not gather with Me, scatters.

"When the unclean spirit goes out of a man, it passes through waterless places seeking rest, and not finding any, it says, 'I will return to my house from which I came.' And when it comes, it finds it swept and put in order. Then it goes and takes along seven other spirits more evil than itself, and they go in and live there; and the last state of that man becomes worse than the first."

Jesus turned toward the elderly Pharisee who had originally asked for a sign and said, "An evil and adulterous generation demands a sign; and yet no sign will be given to it except for the sign of Jonah. For just as Jonah was three days and three nights in the belly of the sea monster, so shall the Son of Man be three days and three nights in the heart of the earth. Just as Jonah became a sign to the Ninevites, so will the Son of Man be a sign to this generation.

"The men of Nineveh will stand up with this generation at the judgment and condemn it because they repented at the preaching of Jonah; and behold, something greater than Jonah is here.

"The Queen of the South will rise up with the men of this generation at the judgment and condemn it, because she came from the ends of the earth to hear the wisdom of Solomon; and behold, something greater than Solomon is here."

The Pharisees are growing angrier by the minute.

Pointing to an oil lamp sitting in the middle of a table, Jesus continued, "No one, after lighting a lamp, puts it away in a cellar nor under a basket, do they? Of course not! Instead, they put it on a lampstand so that those who enter may see the light."

Is He talking about Himself?

"The eye is the lamp of your body; when your eye is clear, your whole body also is full of light; but when it is bad, your body also is full of darkness. Watch out that the light in you is not darkness. If therefore your whole body is full of light, with no dark part in it, it will be wholly illumined, as when the lamp illuminates you with its glow."[7]

While He was still speaking, a young man stepped in the doorway and shouted, "Jesus, Your mother and brothers are standing outside calling to You. They want to speak with You."

Surveying the crowd, Jesus answered, "Who is My mother, and who are My brothers?"

Stretching out His hand and sweeping it across the room, He answered, "Behold, My mother and My brothers! For whoever does the will of My Father who is in heaven, he is My brother and sister and mother."

The Scribes and Pharisees are going to tear Him to shreds over this statement. Most Jewish leaders and most of the people consider the commandment to honor your father and mother as the greatest of all the commandments. To say what Jesus just said is highly offensive to a proper Jewish person.

Just as I suspected, the room erupted like a volcano. The people visibly and vocally expressed their offense. The young man, who brought the message, spun around on his heels to tell Mary how her Son had responded. The Pharisees and Scribes looked very pleased that the Master had spoken in a manner that was so highly offensive to the people.[8]

CHAPTER THREE

Laban asks, "Peter, what were Jesus' mother and brothers doing outside? Why were they not with Him? Did they not know that He was the Messiah?"

"Laban, the truth is they did not understand at all who Jesus was. Of course, Mary knew His birth was supernatural, and she had seen Him turn water into wine and do various miracles, but she was limited in her understanding as to the fullness of Who He was and His purpose for living on earth. As for Jesus' brothers, at this point, they believed Him to be merely a man. It was not until after His death and resurrection that they came to know Him as the Promised One, the Son of God."

"*If* he was the Son of God, how could they grow up with him and not know it?" Eleazer asks with a sarcastic edge to his voice.

"Jesus came in the flesh; He was fully man and fully God, but He was a child just like any other. He played just as you did. He worked just as you did. He looked just like any other Jewish boy in Nazareth. Jesus grew into the statue of a man with His deity hidden. There was an appointed time for that revelation, and until that time, Jesus appeared like all others," I answer.

"Seems strange to me. If I was the Son of God, I would have made sure everyone knew who I was. I would have been born in a castle and had servants waiting on me hand and foot. I would have surrounded myself with luxury and had every comfort this earth had to offer. I would have denied myself no pleasure. I would have conquered nations and acquired the wealth of the world," Eleazer replies.

"I am certainly glad you're not the Son of God," Justus responds.

"As am I," I add. "Eleazer, Jesus demonstrated how we are to live. One of the main characteristics of His life was that He lived in relation to others as though He was a servant. He showed us that life is not about gathering riches, acquiring power or being popular, neither is it about abiding in comfort or having a carefree existence. Jesus came to a world that was in great need as opposed to a world that has all it needs. This world had nothing to offer the Son of God; He did not come to receive, but He came to give. He did not come to be served, but to serve.

"And He knew exactly what He was doing at all times. He had a set time for revealing who He was and for revealing truth, and no one could persuade Him to reveal either sooner than His Father had ordained."

"He *really* was the Son of God!" Justus exclaims.

I chuckle. Justus continues, "The more you tell us about Him, the more real He becomes."

"What about their demand for a sign?" Laban asks.

"The Jews demanded miraculous signs, but I think the most miraculous sign of all was the fact that the Son of God laid aside His garments of light, left His place in heaven and made Himself like His brethren in all things. But, many of the Jews were unable to see and many who did see, were unwilling to accept Him. Jesus was so simple, so kind, so pure that many would not receive Him," I answer.

Eleazer interrupts, "I now know for certain that Jesus could not have been the Son of God!"

"And what do you base that on?" I ask.

"Jesus rejected his very own mother, and then he claimed that those listening to his message were his mother and his brothers and his sisters. Well, the true Messiah would never reject his mother, thus breaking the greatest of all the commandments, which is to honor your father and mother. What Jesus did was clearly contrary to the Law, thus disqualifying him from being the Messiah."

I answer, "Jesus was not rejecting His earthly family but was making the point that anyone who chooses to obey God is just as much a part of His family as His very own mother and brothers."

"And how do you know that?" Eleazer asks.

"His family had come for the purpose of rescuing Him, for they had decided that He was possibly mentally unstable. They reasoned that only a crazy person would preach a message that would bring him toe to toe with the Scribes and Pharisees, which is a battle you cannot win," I answer.

"Did he ever go to his mother and brothers?" Laban inquires.

"He did, but He did not leave with them. He was not going to allow anyone, not even His very own mother, to keep Him from fulfilling the plans that God had for Him. So, He continued teaching and healing the people, and His brothers rejected Him, but His mother followed her Son from town to town. She was silent most of the time, but she watched everything, pondering the things she saw and heard, keeping them hidden in her heart, even to the very end."

"You have not convinced me, Peter," Eleazer responds, "but I have nothing better to do in this God-forsaken place, so tell me more."

I respond, "There is no place on earth forsaken by God, my brother. Remember the words of king David:

"Where can I go from Thy Spirit?
Or where can I flee from Thy presence?
If I ascend to heaven Thou art there;
If I make my bed in Sheol, behold, Thou are there.
If I take the wings of the dawn,
If I dwell in the remotest part of the sea,
Even there Thy hand will lead me,
and Thy right hand will lay hold of me.
If I say, "Surely the darkness will overwhelm me,
and the light around me will be night."
Even the darkness is not dark to Thee
and the night is as bright as the day.
Darkness and light are alike to Thee.[9]

"No, Eleazer, God is even in this place."

"If that's what you want to believe, then that is your privilege," Eleazer replies.

Josiah interrupts saying, "Peter, I was just wondering how you are feeling? How's your leg?"

"My leg is swollen and very painful. My body is racked with fever, but suffering has long since become my friend, and God's grace is sufficient," I answer.[10]

"Suffering is a fool's friend, and you, Peter, are—," Eleazer angrily responds.

"Then call me a fool!" I interrupt. "I will gladly be a fool for Christ!"

Justus joins in, "Eleazer, do you not have a heart? Where is your sensitivity? Does nothing touch you?"

"I have a heart, but it is a heart built of stone, not the heart of some old man who believes every story he hears and blindly follows. No, I have seen much in my lifetime, and one thing I have learned is to live by my intellect not by my feelings. Emotions are for fools, old women and children," Eleazer answers.

"What makes you so angry? What has happened in your life to make you so callous?" Laban asks.

"That is of no concern to you," Eleazer abruptly answers.

"Lest we create a disturbance that would be unprofitable for all, I propose that we turn our attention back to the King," I state wiping the sweat from my forehead.

"Do so if you like, but not for my sake. I need nothing from you, and certainly have no desire to hear your stories," Eleazer responds.

"You need to hear them much more than you know," Justus quietly says.

"And you don't?" Eleazer mocks.

"Peter, perhaps now would be a good time to return to the story, if you are up to it?" Justus asks clearly irritated.

CHAPTER FOUR

After speaking with His mother and brothers, Jesus led us to the lake where we relaxed by the sea and broke bread. It was a beautiful spring day.

Jesus remarked, "Look at the fields. Are they not dressed in garments even more glorious than those of Solomon?"

I looked where He pointed. Nearby, the bright green grass was adorned with blood-red anemones, colorful tulips, glorious narcissus and snow-white lilies. Like a refreshing drink, I took in the beautiful scenery and peaceful surroundings.

God must certainly appreciate beauty, for He has placed us in a Masterpiece.

I looked back at Jesus and saw that He, too, appreciated the view before us, but it was short-lived because a large group of people were headed our way.

Jesus whispered, "The crowd will be great; it will be better to speak to them from the boat."

Wasting no time, we hurried to the sea and acquired a boat. Jesus sat in the prow and waited. I surveyed the crowd gathering on the gently sloping shoreline, which made for the perfect theatre.

Most of the crowd were rural peasants and sheep herders, for such is the majority of Galilee's population.

It never ceased to amaze me how selflessly Jesus served and how freely He showed lovingkindness to the poor, to those who were considered the least of society.

Jesus began His sermon by pointing to a man who was casting seed in a nearby field. He said, "Listen! A farmer went out to plant his seed. As he was planting, some seed fell into one of the many footpaths in the field; the birds came and ate them up. But, some of the seed fell on the soil of the field.

"The seed sprouted quickly because the soil was so shallow; but when the sun came up, the young plants were scorched, and since their roots were not deep, they dried up.

"Other seed fell among thorns, which grew up and choked it; so that it yielded no grain. But other seed fell into good, fertile, deep soil, and it flourished. It sprouted and grew and yielded a crop—thirty, sixty, even a hundred times what was sown."

Most of Israel's soil has only a thin layer of dirt over a shelf of limestone rock. To find a field with deep soil is a treasure indeed. But, to have a hundredfold crop is unheard of! No one gets a hundredfold crop!

Climbing out of the boat Jesus exclaimed, "Whoever has ears to hear, let him hear!"

The people looked as perplexed as I was. Jesus seemed not to notice that they did not understand His parable and dismissed the crowd.

Jesus led the way to my house. Along the way, Andrew asked, "Master, why do You speak to the multitude in parables?"

Jesus answered, "Because it has been given to you to

know the secrets of the Kingdom of Heaven, but it has not been given to them."

His response caused me to feel quite important. Jesus glanced my way and continued, "Anyone who has a little will be given more, so that he has plenty; but from those who have nothing, even what he does have will be taken away."

This I do not understand.

In a voice filled with longing, Jesus said, "My friends, this is why I speak in parables—the people look, but choose not to see. They listen, but choose not to hear.

"When Isaiah brought God's message to your forefathers, the people were so dull of heart that you would have thought that God Himself had shut their ears, their eyes and their minds. Well, My friends, the people are like that today. They hear My words, but do not listen."

I suppose this would be like a Lover who has a priceless gift to give, but upon giving the gift realizes that the one He loves has set her affections on another.

Jesus walked on in silence.

I know well the passage that Jesus spoke of. It is from the writings of Isaiah which says, "You will keep on hearing, but will not understand; you will keep on seeing, but will not perceive; for the heart of this people has become dull. With their ears they scarcely hear, and they have closed their eyes, otherwise they would see with their eyes, hear with their ears, understand with their heart, and then turn and I would heal them."[11]

I actually think that I understand what Jesus is saying. He is saying that God did not intend for the people to be so dull. It was not His doing, but the people have made themselves so dull that they cannot hear and neither can they understand.

Jesus interrupted my thoughts saying, "Andrew, Peter, James, all twelve of you are blessed to see what you now see and to hear what you now hear. I am telling you the truth: many prophets and righteous men desired to see what you see, but did not see it. They desired to hear what you hear, but they did not hear it."

I asked, "But Master, what good does it do for us to hear the parables if we do not understand them?"

Jesus invited us to rest under the shade of a nearby fig tree, which we eagerly did. I stretched out on the tall grass and took a long drink from my water bag. Jesus leaned His head back against the tree trunk and sighed. Propping myself up on my elbow, I looked His way.

I could spend eternity with this Man and never be bored. He is like a rock, He never changes, and yet I never know what He is going to do.

Jesus looked at each of us and said, "It has been given to you to know the secrets of the Kingdom of heaven."

I like secrets.

"But I must first take care of a situation," He said as He picked up a stick and flung it at a nearby bush. Immediately, a large, black snake slithered out from under the low lying branches and into the clearing. I quickly got out of its path as did the others with the exception of Judas.

I've never liked snakes.

The snake paused raising its ugly head.

Did that thing just look at Jesus with a defiant look?

Jesus waved His hand, and the snake continued on.

How did Jesus know that snake was there? He couldn't have seen it, and He certainly didn't hear it. Is there no end to His knowledge?

Once the snake was out of sight, Jesus continued, "Now, I will explain to you the parable of the sower. The farmer plants God's message like seeds that are strewn along the ground, but Satan lies in wait in order to steal the message."

Jesus paused long enough to look at the place where the snake had been hiding. He then continued, "When anyone hears the word of the Kingdom and does not understand it, the evil one comes and snatches away what has been sown in his heart. This is the one on whom seed was sown beside the road.

"And the one on whom seed was sown on the rocky places is like the man who hears the good news and immediately receives it with joy; yet he has no firm root in himself but remains true only temporarily, and when affliction or persecution comes because of the message, immediately he falls away.

"The one on whom seed was sown among the thorns and weeds, this is the man who hears that the Kingdom has come, but the worries of this age and the deceitfulness of riches choke out the word, and he becomes unfruitful.

"Those seeds which were planted on good soil are the people who listen to the message, understand and obey it. These will produce fruit—some one-hundredfold, some sixty, and some thirty."

Now I understand!

Standing, Jesus said, "Come, let us resume our journey."

With much to ponder, we walked the short distance to my house in silence. My lovely wife, Miriam, and her mother quickly prepared a feast for us. As the sun set, we reclined around the table to indulge in the wonderful food and enjoy the delightful fellowship.

Once we had eaten and were satisfied, Jesus rose from the table and took a stick from the cook fire, which He used to light a lamp He had placed on the table. "Do you light a lamp so that you can put it under a basket or under the bed?" He asked.

"No one would be so foolish," I answered.

"Rightly you have answered. A lamp is supposed to be put in a place where it is visible so that it will shed its light for all to see. In the same way, truth is meant to be seen, not to be hidden or concealed!

"Know this, every thing that is hidden will become clear, and every secret thing will be made known."

That could be painful.

"If a person has ears to hear with, he should use them! But, My friends, be careful what you hear."

How is that possible? How am I to be careful what I hear?

"You will be measured by the standard of measure you use to judge others! Whoever has, to him shall more be given; but this will happen to the person who has almost nothing—even what he thinks he has will be taken away from him.

"The kingdom of God is like this: A man puts seed in the ground. The seed comes up and grows while he sleeps at night and while he goes about his day. The man does not understand how this happens. The earth produces fruit with help from no one. The shoot comes first, then the ear, then the full corn. When the crop is ready, the man cuts it with a sickle; harvest time has come.

"What is the Kingdom of God like? What can I compare it with? It is like the mustard seed, which someone put in the ground. It is one of the smallest seeds on earth, but after it is planted and comes up, it is one of the largest garden plants, producing great branches that even wild birds build nests in so that they are protected from the sun and weather."

Surely He is comparing Israel to a mustard tree, for we started out a small people and have become a great nation, but what is this talk of wild birds building their nests in our branches? Can others who are not of us become one with us? They cannot be grafted in, can they? It appears that He is insinuating that the Messianic Kingdom will include a nation other than Israel, but this cannot be! The Jews alone are God's chosen people.

Jesus' face was radiant as He spoke. His eyes seemed

to peer into a world that only He could see, a world that delighted His soul.

He thoroughly enjoys bringing light to a fallen world.

He picked up a piece of bread and said, "The Kingdom of heaven is like leaven, which a woman took and hid in three pecks of flour until it was all leavened."

The Kingdom message is frequently discussed in every Jewish home and at nearly every public meeting. But, we view the Kingdom in terms of power and authority. Our religious leaders believe that if the people of Israel would diligently obey their rules, traditions and regulations, then the Messiah would surely notice our piety and come to our aid.

We know that when He comes, He will overthrow the Romans, delivering us from their offensive rule in such a glorious manner that all the nations of the earth will see and voluntarily come under the rule of Israel. Then Jerusalem will become the world capital, and the Messiah's Kingdom would be a time of world peace. Everyone knows that this is how it will be; therefore, we long for His arrival that we might be delivered from our enemies and take our rightful place among the nations.

Perhaps this is what He means by the Kingdom being like leaven.

Placing the bread back on the platter, Jesus blessed Miriam and her mother, bidding them good-night. He then retired to the rooftop. I followed, as did the others. As Jesus unrolled His pallet, I asked, "Master, would You explain to us the parable concerning the tares of the field?"

"Most certainly. The one who sows the good seed is the Son of Man, and the field is the world; and as for the good seed, these are the sons of the Kingdom; and the weeds and thorns are the sons of the evil one; and the enemy who sowed them is the devil, and the harvest is the end of the age; and the reapers are angels.

"Just as the weeds are gathered and burned with fire, so shall it be at the end of the age. The Son of Man will send forth His angels, and they will gather out of His Kingdom all stumbling blocks and those who commit lawlessness and will throw them into the furnace of fire; in that place, there will be weeping and gnashing of teeth. Then the righteous will shine forth as the sun in the Kingdom of their Father. He who has ears to hear, let him hear!"

"I must admit that I do not understand Your message of the Kingdom," I said.

He responded, "The Kingdom of heaven is like a treasure hidden in a field, which a man found and hid again; and from joy over it he goes and sells all that he has and buys that field.

Is the man in this analogy the Messiah who found Israel and, in His delight, will sell everything He has in order to redeem her?

Or perhaps the man is the person who discovers the Kingdom and, realizing what a glorious treasure he has found, sells everything he has in order to be part of such a Kingdom? I did that very thing; I left my fishing business in order to follow the Master.

"Again, the Kingdom of heaven is like a merchant seeking fine pearls, and upon finding a pearl of great value, he went and sold all that he had and bought the pearl.

"Again, the Kingdom of heaven is like a dragnet cast into the sea, which gathered fish of every kind. When the net was filled, they drew it up on the beach; and they sat down and gathered the good fish into containers, but the bad they threw away. So it will be at the end of the age; the angels will come and take out the wicked from among the righteous, and will throw them into the furnace of fire where there will be weeping and gnashing of teeth.

"Now do you understand all these things?"

We answered, "Yes."

"Therefore every scribe who has become a citizen of the Kingdom of heaven is like the head of a household, who brings out both old and new coins from his strongbox, which he keeps hidden in his house.[12]

"Because you are members of this Kingdom, you are victorious. You are no longer a victim because of your King who causes all things to work together for good to those who love God and are called according to His purpose."[13]

Exhausted, I fought to stay awake. The last thing I heard the Master say was, "If you are part of this Kingdom, your righteousness will exceed what you see in the Pharisees. Instead of patting yourself on the back because you have not murdered anyone, you will diligently work to get hatred out of your heart. You will love your enemies, which includes your Roman oppressors. Instead of congratulating yourself for not committing adultery, you will live in such a way as to not even look on a woman to lust after her. Instead of doing good deeds in order to be noticed by men, your deeds will be done in secret so that your Father who sees in secret will give you the reward. This is the nature and character of those who are citizens of the Kingdom of God."[14]

I closed my eyes to think about His challenging and strange description of Kingdom life, but I fell asleep before I could even form one intelligent thought.

The obnoxious crowing of a rooster woke me before it was even daylight.

"We should cook that bird for dinner," I mumbled to myself as I rolled over.

Lifting my head, I discovered that Jesus had already risen. Hurrying down the stairs, I found Jesus in a serious conversation with Miriam and her mother, who were so engaged that they did not notice me until I laid my hand of my wife's shoulder.

Miriam looked up; tears filled her eyes. Seeing my concern, she exclaimed, "These are tears of joy that you see!"

Wiping her eyes on her sleeve, Miriam stood and said, "Those who labor because of love work a lot harder and considerably longer than slaves who work only because they have no choice."

"What?" I asked quite puzzled.

"Slaves can only lead others to a master, but a child can lead others to a Father, and a bride can lead others to the one she loves."

"What are you talking about?"

"Only those things that I have learned this morning," she answered over her shoulder as she and her mother hurried off to prepare breakfast.

I sat before the greatest Teacher I have ever known and asked, "Will I ever understand the deep mysteries You speak of?"

"The day will come when you will understand greater things than these, My friend."

"But Your messages are foreign. Your ways are far greater, far nobler, far richer than any people I have ever known."

"Exactly," He answered.

At this point, the rest of the apostles joined us.

"My ways are indeed higher than your ways, and My thoughts are higher than your thoughts," Jesus went on to say.

"Having walked with You, I can believe that," I responded.

"My love is greater than the ocean and My mercy is higher than the heavens. Neither have a beginning or an ending."

"How is that possible? Everything begins somewhere and ends somewhere," I responded.

Miriam called us to the table.

"Not everything, Peter," Jesus answered. His eyes sparkled like one who knows a grand secret and longs to share it.

"What has no beginning or ending?" I asked.

"God."

Before I could respond, Matthew commented, "Jesus, You are so much more than an excellent, skilled carpenter."

"You are so much more than a brilliant Teacher," Andrew added.

Again, Miriam called.

"You are the kindest Man I have ever known," John said.

"And the wisest," I added.

Miriam walked into the room; a beautiful smile lit up her face. She waved a basket filled with hot bread. The wonderful aroma drew us like honey draws bees.

And that's one smart woman.

As we reclined around the table, Jesus shared stories from of old. He spoke of Abraham, Moses and Elijah as though He personally knew them. It seemed as though He was there when Abraham laid his son on the altar, when Moses parted the Red Sea and when Elijah left this world in a fiery chariot.

How can a simple, uneducated carpenter know the things He knows? And where did He get the depth of compassion, wisdom and understanding that He has?

"My friends, let Me tell you of the time when Abraham called his faithful servant to his side and instructed him to find a suitable partner for his son, Isaac.

"Some time later, as Isaac was pacing back and forth in the fields watching and hoping and longing, he saw his father's servant returning. Just behind him, was the most beautiful woman he had ever seen. When Rebekah saw him, she quickly drew her veil over her face, but it was too late. Isaac had already seen her and with just one look, she had stolen his heart! Oh, how Isaac rejoiced, for this was the day he had been waiting for, this was the day of the gladness of his heart! And so it will be for the Son of Man when He comes into His kingdom."

Is Jesus trying to tell us that He is going to get married?! That isn't possible—He's not even betrothed! There must be another explanation.

Rebekah represents Israel, for we know that God has clearly called Israel His bride. But, what is this talk of the Son of Man, the Messiah looking for a bride when He comes? Is He to have a bride? If so, who?

Jesus stood, interrupting my thoughts. He led us into the streets where we spent the entire day among the crowds as He taught and healed the sick. Near the close of day, He dismissed the crowds and instructed us to depart to the other side of the sea.

As soon as we pushed the boat from the shore, Jesus, thoroughly exhausted, laid down on the bench in the stern, which is the place reserved for distinguished people or honored guests. In the short time it took to raise the sails, Jesus had already fallen asleep.

As usual, Andrew took the helmsman's position, and we headed out to sea. My thoughts were not on my work; I could do this with my eyes closed. No, my thoughts were on the sea and the beauty surrounding me. It was such a nice evening. The sky was clear, the stars were just beginning to shine, and the water was as smooth and slick as glass.

Oh, how peaceful it was! No clamoring crowds, no hustle and bustle of the cities, no rocky, dusty roads, and best of all, no Pharisees or Scribes trying to trap Jesus! I have missed the smell of the sea, the feel of the wind on my face and the sound of water lapping against the sides of the boat.

How refreshing!

The Sea of Galilee is a small body of water, about thirteen miles long by six miles wide. It lies in a deep hollow surrounded on all sides by steep ranges of beautiful hills. On the upper hills, it is quite cool, but at the lake, which is much lower, it is hot and humid. Because of the difference in temperatures, storms often and unexpectedly descend on the sea and can be as fierce and unrelenting as the war between good and evil.

In spite of the violent storms, I have always loved the sea. As soon as I was old enough to walk, my father took me with him on his fishing boat. It was then, at such a young age that I came to love this ever changing sea.

Andrew threw me the end of a rope, startling me.

"Dreaming, are you?" he asked, laughing.

"Just remembering," I answered as I tied off the sails.

"You miss the sea?" he asked.

"Yeah."

"Me, too," Andrew replied as he stood beside me. "Simon, do you ever regret walking away from our uncomplicated, predictable, normal way of life?"

"Well, I don't know that I'd call it uncomplicated, predictable or normal. Perhaps in comparison to a life with Jesus it may seem that way. I can't say that I regret walking away from it, but there are times when I wonder if I did the right thing. Mostly because I don't exactly understand what I have become a part of. And, truthfully, I do not know how this thing is going to end. After all, Jesus is not your typical rabbi. He is merciful, good and kind. He is constant, consistent and always the same, but He is the most unpredictable Man I have ever known," I answer.

Having secured the sails, I joined Andrew. Leaning my head back against the side of the boat, I asked, "What about you, Andrew, do you regret leaving all this behind?"

"I have no regrets, Simon. Where else could I go?"

John joined in saying, "I cannot imagine living my life any other way. Where else could I find One who comes face to face with my weaknesses and my faults, and still accepts me? What does this world have to offer that is better than just one glance of His kind eyes? What better thing is there to be gained than the affections of this Man? Show me the finest gold in the world, the purest silver, the largest kingdom, the deepest ocean, the rarest jewels, and I will gladly refuse them for just one day with Jesus!"

I was speechless.

For one so young, John certainly has planted his feet deeply and given his heart fully.

I closed my eyes as John and Andrew continued the conversation. So much has happened in such a short time. I no longer believed many of the things I grew up believing. As a matter of fact, I was not exactly sure what I believed anymore. The Master had turned my world upside down. There was a time when I thought all I would ever be was a fisherman, but all of that has changed; I have changed.

I looked at Jesus; the soft light from the full moon illumined His face. He was in a deep sleep, which did not surprise me considering the fact that He spends most of His days ministering to the multitudes and then spends much of His nights in prayer.

Jesus was relentless and fierce in His devotion to both God and man. And yet, His loving service was never random, neither was it orchestrated by chance or by man. Exactly how He determined what He did, I was not exactly sure. I only knew that He was very decided in all that He did and everywhere He went. He never wavered, and neither did He wander aimlessly day or night.

A gentle breeze swept across me, showering me with a fine mist. The lapping of the water against the boat was music to my ears.

The stars were absolutely brilliant.

The breeze has picked up. The sails are full. With a healthy wind like this we should make good time.

Andrew and John were still deep in conversation. Judas, Thomas, Bartholomew and Matthew snored loudly. The others were either asleep or deep in thought; I was not sure which.

The wind is definitely picking up.

I looked up at the sky; a few clouds were beginning to veil the stars. I pulled my cloak closer as sea water sprayed me again.

John suddenly stood, and carefully stepping over Bartholomew, removed his outer garment and covered Jesus with it.

He is so attentive; I wish I had thought of doing that!

In response to the ever increasing wind, the waves rose up to make their presence known, but Jesus slept on in perfect peace.

Does the Master dream? If so, what fills the canvas of His mind? Battles? Thrones? Kingdoms? Power? Riches?

Suddenly, an angry gust hit our boat tossing it as easily as a child tosses a ball. I jumped to my feet as did the other apostles; we were all too familiar with what this meant.

Within moments, a furious storm was upon us. The winds threatened to capsize us as the waves filled the boat with water. We quickly pulled down the sails, but it made little difference. I glanced at Jesus; He slept soundly.

I was nearly knee deep in water, holding fast to a rope with one hand and bailing water with the other. A storm was raging, the boat was sinking, and the Master slept!

What kind of Man is this?

I fought against the storm in order to get to the stern. After much effort, falling on my knees, I shook Jesus trying to wake Him. "Master! Help us! We're sinking!" I cried.

With those words, a large wave slapped the side of the

boat, nearly flipping us over. Jesus sat up and looked around. His expression was that of perfect peace.

There is not a trace of fear in His eyes. He is not in the least bit concerned.

Laying His hand on my shoulder, He asked, "Simon, why are you afraid?"

I looked around at the raging sea and our sinking boat and responded, "Master, I have good reason to be afraid—we are all about to drown!"

With a gentle squeeze of my shoulder, He responded, "So little trust you have!"

His eyes were filled with kindness and confidence.

He stood, stretched out His hand and rebuked the winds and the waves. Immediately, they bowed their knee to the Master, and perfect peace returned to the sky and sea.[15]

Shocked, stunned and amazed, I slowly stood to my feet. Everything was completely and perfectly still. Everything, that is, except for my physical body, which was shaking violently.

Who is this Jesus?!

I fell down before Him.

With a smile, He nodded and then laid back down announcing, "Set sail for the Gadarenes territory."

He sat back up and said, "And thank you, John, for covering Me with your garment."

With my mouth hanging open, I turned to John who looked like a deer caught in torchlights. "How did He know?" John whispered.

I shrugged.

Within minutes, Jesus was sound asleep.

I stared off into the darkness. James and John were beside me. Turning to them I said, "What kind of Man is this that even the winds and the sea obey Him?"

"A Man unlike any I have ever known," James answered.

"A Man in whom is found everything," John added.

"A Man who has connections in high places," Judas stated.

"A Man like none other," I said.

"Let's get these sails up," Andrew interrupted.

I helped raise the sails, but my mind was definitely in another place. As Jesus slept soundly, we bailed water.

It was still dark when Jesus woke. "We will arrive in the Gadarenes territory in about an hour," I announced.

He nodded, staring into the darkness.

Strange that the Master would choose to go to such an undesirable place as the Gadarenes territory, which is mostly made up of Gentiles. I suppose He is just trying to get away from the crowds and their relentless demands.

Jesus was soaking wet. He had slept on a rough, wooden bench, the springtime air was cool, and yet He did not complain. As a matter of fact, I do not believe I have ever heard Jesus complain about anything or anyone. Neither have I ever heard Him speak an unkind word about anyone.

What is it that motivates this One to live such a holy life?

I obviously drifted off to sleep because the next thing I knew Andrew was announcing that we had arrived at our destination. Within minutes, our boat scrubbed the sea floor. Thomas and Phillip quickly jumped out and dragged us inland. Matthew dropped the anchor.

Sitting up, I rubbed my eyes and then rubbed them again. To my horror, we had landed at a burial ground!

"Master, we should turn around—now!" I whispered, afraid to disturb whatever spirits might be lurking in the caves.

Jesus merely peered into the darkness. He seemed to be looking for someone or something. Like a man with his eye on the finish line, He jumped out of the boat, landing with a splash in the shallow water. Turning for a brief moment, He motioned for us to follow. Looking back at the others who were looking at me, I forced a courageous smile, shrugged and then threw my leg over the side.

I will never be accused of being a coward.

Jesus walked a short distance and then stopped to wait for us, for which I was most grateful. I admit that I was walking slowly, for I wanted to be close to that boat should the need arise for a speedy departure.

Jesus stood on the rocky beach, in the moonlight, just a few feet from numerous caves that held the bodies of dead people and provided a haven for evil spirits.

"It's not too late to turn around," I whispered as we came alongside Him.

Strange noises to my right caused me to press a little closer to the Master. Jesus responded, "It is only a herd of swine, Simon."

To my relief, I could see that He was right. There was a very large herd of swine sleeping nearby.

Why has He brought us here? For what purpose? All that is here are pigs and the dead, both of which are forbidden for Jewish people to be anywhere near. Surely, there has been some mistake. Surely, Jesus cannot mean for us to walk through this place?

I turned to once again inform the Master of the wisdom of returning to the boat when a deep guttural sound came from the closest of the caves. The hair on my arms stood on end. Terrified, yet not wanting to admit it, I commanded my feet not to run.

Slowly turning my head in the direction of the sound, I saw two pairs of eyes staring right at us. I stumbled backwards, but Jesus remained fixed, stroking His beard as He looked on, undaunted.

Another growl. I took several steps back tripping over James and Andrew. Jesus stepped forward, heading directly toward the tomb. The two pair of eyes widened as they watched His steady and determined approach from the confines of their deep darkness.

What is looking at us? Is it man, beast or ghost?

I suddenly realized that my knees were shaking.

John and James stepped out from behind me and hurried after Jesus. The other apostles followed after them. Not wanting to be the only coward, I hurried after them.

Slowly emerging out of the deep darkness were what appeared to be two men. They shrieked as if in pain as the moonlight fell on their faces. Stopping just outside the mouth of the tomb, they crouched on all fours as they closely watched our slow but steady approach. After a few minutes, one of them began picking the bugs off of his arm and eating them.

We were now close enough to see that they were both naked and covered in layers of filth. Their long hair was matted to their heads and necks. A steady flow of foam ran into their beards. Numerous cuts, both old and new, covered their bodies. Both men had manacles around their wrists and ankles—the chains long since broken. Never had I seen such a fearful sight among men or beast!

The man who was eating bugs decided to find another way to entertain himself. He selected a sharp stone and sat back on his haunches. Studying his legs with the greatest of attention, he finally found just the right place and began carving away the flesh; blood flowed freely down his leg. Within minutes the fresh wound was covered with flies and other blood-loving insects. The man soon searched for a new place to carve.

This is no man; he is nothing more than an animal! Why has Jesus brought us here? For what purpose? Certainly not for these animals, these creatures!

I turned to leave, but Jesus reached out and touched me. I looked into His kind eyes. "Simon, those who are well need no Physician."

"But, Master?"

"Never make a decision based on fear, Peter."

I looked back at the two despicable creatures. One pair of inhuman eyes remained fixed on Jesus while the other continued mutilating itself.

Suddenly, like a madman, the pair of eyes came to life, and a bloodcurdling scream escaped his mouth. With a leap, the madman came toward us. Jesus remained unmoved; I was ready to bolt. The man cutting himself crouched forward, watching closely.

The crazy man stopped just short of Jesus and sniffed the air like an animal. A low, guttural growl came from the depths of his being. Slowly, and without taking his eyes off Jesus, he picked up a rather large stone. Standing upright, he cursed, all the while spewing foam. Jesus remained unmoved; His face displayed nothing but compassion. Trembling, the madman slung the stone on the ground, and in a moment of sanity, he fell at Jesus' feet, bowing low before Him.

"Unclean spirit, come out of this man," Jesus quietly said.

In a voice that was straight from the abyss, the man responded, "What do you want with me, Jesus, Son of God? I implore You in God's name, don't torture me!"

"What is your name?" Jesus asked.

"Legion because there are so many of us. We beg you not to send us out of this region," the man answered.

Legion? A legion is 6,000 troops! Could it be possible that this man has 6,000 demons living inside of him?

The man who had been cutting himself lunged toward Jesus and shouted, "Send us to the pigs! Yes, that is it! Allow us to go into them!"

"Go, then," Jesus commanded.

Immediately, both men's faces contorted, and they fell over as if dead. Suddenly, the pigs started squealing and running into each other as they raced down the hillside. I watched in disbelief as the entire herd ran over the cliff and sank like millstones into the sea. The man who had been cutting himself suddenly jumped up and ran away.

The swine keepers, who watched from the hilltop, stood with their mouths open wide in disbelief. Coming to their senses, they ran away. I turned back to Jesus whose attention had never left the man lying prostrate at His feet. He knelt beside him, His face turned heavenward. Placing His hand on the man's back, He said, "You are now free, My friend."

The man lifted his head rather slowly. His eyes were now clear, and his countenance had been transformed. There was something childlike in his manner now, something innocent. The man touched Jesus' face with his filthy hands as if he were checking to see if He was real. And then, the man smiled, probably for the first time in a long time.

Jesus returned his smile and said, "You are not dreaming. I am real."

The man nodded.

What an amazing transformation in such a short time!

Jesus removed His outer garment and laid it over the man's shoulders, covering his nakedness. Taking the man's dirt-caked hand, He raised him up and led him to a nearby rock where they sat together. I stayed close to the Master for two reasons: one, there were other creatures lurking in the dark tombs; and two, I wanted to hear what was said.

As the two engaged in conversation, I could not believe how intelligently the man responded.

Only moments ago, this man was possessed by a legion of demons, and now he is speaking in his right mind!

As Jesus answered the man's many questions, the morning sun peeked its head over the horizon, enabling me to see more clearly the man's condition; I was appalled! He was covered with massive scars, cuts and bruises!

He must have been in that horrible state for a very long time.

No one noticed that John had gone back to the boat until he returned with his satchel slung over his shoulder. Stopping beside this miracle of a man, John pulled out his only change of clothes and offered them to him. The man who was clearly surprised and overwhelmed by his kindness, simply nodded.

As he dressed, he identified himself as Syrus. Returning the Master's garment, he thanked John for his new clothes. He then said, "I am forever grateful to You for rescuing me from my endless torment, my Lord."

Hearing quite a commotion, we looked up and saw people gathering on the hilltop. The swine keepers, who had run away, now stood in the midst of them.

They must have spread the news of the pigs destruction and this man's deliverance.

A man from the crowd shouted out, "Is this not the demoniac who lived in the burial caves?"

Another answered, "It is indeed. This is the same man who was a terror and torment to himself and to everyone who dared to come near this place. But, look at him now!"

"Who is the man who set the demoniac free?" a young man shouted.

Syrus jumped to his feet and answered, "His name is Jesus, and He is the Messiah! And because of Him, I am free!"

Another voice, quite angry, shouted out, "People, let us not forget about the destruction that has occurred here today! Because of this 'Messiah' over two thousand swine are dead and lying at the bottom of the lake! If he stays in our midst, what other things will he destroy?"

"Yeah, what other things will he do?" another shouted.

Jesus appeared unaffected by their accusatory words, but not Syrus who was angrily pacing back and forth. He was about to respond, but Jesus motioned for him to be still. Syrus conceded, but continued to pace mumbling under his breath.

Several very wealthy and important-looking men arrived and identified themselves as the owners of the pigs. As they looked at their pigs now floating in the water and washing up on the beach, anger filled their voices. It was then that I realized we were in trouble.

"Master," I said.

"Yes, Peter?"

"Perhaps, we should go now," I responded pointing to the men.

"Not yet, Peter, not yet," Jesus answered.

The men turned to the crowd and skillfully built a case against Jesus. As a result, a delegation was sent pleading with Him to depart while the others angrily shouted for Him to leave.

With a nod, Jesus announced, "Now, we will depart."

As we made our way back to the boat, Syrus closely followed pleading with Jesus and saying, "Lord, I know that I am not worthy and never could hope to be, but perhaps, out of the depths of your great compassion, You would allow this old stump of a man to come with You? I promise to serve You for the rest of my life."

Syrus's eyes were filled with anticipation; his hands trembled. Stopping just at the water's edge, Jesus turned and placed both His hands on Syrus's shoulders. Looking deep into his eyes, Jesus responded, "My friend, go home to your family and to your friends and to your people. Tell them how much God, in His great mercy, has done for you. In this way, you can best serve Me."

Syrus stepped back as understanding filled his eyes. With a broad grin and an energetic nod, he responded, "Yes, Jesus, that is exactly what I shall do! I shall tell everyone I meet and everyone in the surrounding towns what God has done for me!"

With arms waving wildly, he ran into the curious crowd proclaiming as he went the goodness of God to a lost and dying world.[16]

CHAPTER FIVE

Josiah asks, "Peter, did Jesus know that demonized man was there, or was it just a coincidence?"

With a chuckle, I answer, "With Jesus, there is no such thing as coincidence. He knows everything, even what you are thinking. He knows what was, what is and what is to come. He knew that Syrus was there and He purposely went there that He might offer him deliverance from Satan's torment and prison."

"Your story is ridiculous! Why would Jesus cross the sea at night for one man? Jesus was tired; He had not eaten! No man in their right mind would do such a thing!" Eleazer says with an angry edge to his voice.

"Jesus is not like us, my friend. To Him, every individual is just as important as a multitude. He finds no price too great to pay for a soul. He is the good Shepherd who leaves the ninety-nine sheep in order to go after the one who has lost its way," I answer.

"I'm so glad that Jesus is like this, for it gives me hope," Laban adds.

"We would all be in a good deal of trouble if Jesus was

not who He is," I respond.

"Peter, it sounded to me like the demons in that man knew who Jesus was. They believed that Jesus was the Son of God just as I believe. So, what is the difference?" Josiah asks.

"It is not knowledge but love that distinguishes men from demons, my friend. The demons believe and tremble, but they do not love. That is a privilege only man has. We have the honor and privilege of giving Jesus our voluntary affection. And what a tragedy it would be for the Son of Man not to have the affection of those He died for."

"He certainly deserves more than I have to offer, Josiah interjects.

"'Tis true for all of us," I reply. "My friends, have you ever taken a good look at this amazing earth we call home? There are a multitude of stars in the sky, all of which were created by God. There are countless grains of sand in the sea, also created by God. There are numerous varieties of animals, birds and plants, all created by God.

"This God who spoke into existence this world and all it contains is the same God who invites us to enter into a covenant with Him where we become His eternal partner both now and forever. It is a mystery too great to fathom that One so powerful, so wonderful, so awesome, so glorious would invite weak human beings to be part of His family, to be His eternal Bride, His glorious partner.

"And when we say, 'Yes,' to His invitation, He welcomes us into His family, making us the only created beings who have the privilege of calling Him, 'Father.' The angels in heaven do not have that privilege, neither do any other created beings. We, alone, have the privilege of loving Him and being loved by Him.

"And trust me, my friends, there is a day is coming when Jesus will return to make wrong things right and to judge the earth. On that day, He will separate good from evil and establish His Kingdom on earth. And those who know Him will rule and reign with Him forever."

"My desire is to love Jesus in the same way He loves me," Josiah replies.

"That is a desire worthy of attention, my friends. The only way to love Him in that way is to know Him," I answer.

"Then tell me more that I might know Him more intimately," Josiah pleads.

Eleazer mockingly imitates, "Tell me more that I might know him more intimately."

"Eleazer, if you only knew how much you are loved, you would not be doing what you are doing," I respond.

"I don't care!" he shouts. "I don't care about this man you claim to be some kind of god! I am going to die, and I am perfectly content to do so! I deserve to die ! I deserve to be punished because I robbed and killed my neighbor!

"So, go ahead! Tell me another heart-wrenching story about this too-good-to-be-true Jesus! Tell me something that will make me feel better, something that will take away my guilt if you can! Where's your magic formula? Where's your words of wisdom and cute little sayings? Where's the parable that will fix my horrific mistake?

"Tell me, Peter, can your Jesus turn back the hands of time and give me a second chance? Can he rewrite history? Can he raise the man I killed from the grave? Can he somehow repair the devastation that my actions have brought to my neighbor's wife and her young children? And what about my wife and children, can he restore to them what I took from them in one angry moment?"

Wanting to comfort him, I drag my swollen and very painful leg behind me.

"Do not come near me! I don't want your pity or your advice or your Jesus! I only want one thing and that is to right the wrong I have done, but that would take a *real* miracle, which is something that I am fresh out of! Anything less than this and I am not interested!" he yells.

Ignoring his protest, I continue to draw near saying, "Eleazer, this is probably not what you want to hear, but there is One who can help you, One who can make wrong things right."

He responds, "Your solution is based on a fantasy, but my life is painfully real. There are two families that have been ruined because of me. I am soon to be executed, which is exactly what I deserve and is the only thing that can put me out of my misery. So, leave me! Leave me, I said!"

Furious, he kicks at me and his foot lands flat against my broken leg. Sharp, shooting pain runs through my leg and up my body like lightening courses through a tree. I fall over as the room spins out of control.

Oh, God help me!

In an effort to ease the pain, I try to move my leg to a more comfortable position but find that any position is unbearable.

Father, I desperately need Your help! I need You!

"Peter, what has happened?" Josiah asks.

I cannot answer. I dare not move.

"Peter, are you okay?" Laban asks.

Jesus, help me!

"I think I kicked his broken leg," Eleazer responds.

"You what?!" Justus exclaims.

"You heard me!" Eleazer shouts.

"How could you do such a thing?" Laban asks.

"You don't think that I meant to do it, do you?"

"Peter," Laban asks, "are you okay?"

Oh, God how I need You!

"Let's pray," Laban says.

Father, You are the only One who can help me!

I force myself to focus on Jesus rather than the pain as prayers are being offered on my behalf.

Jesus, I love you! I am safe in Your arms. You are my

strength and my song. You are the reason I live. You are my King and You shall reign forevermore. Mighty God, glorious King, I need You.

Thankfully, the room finally stops spinning, but my leg screams in pain.

Laban asks, "Peter, are you okay?"

"I will be," I force myself to answer.

"We will keep praying," Josiah responds.

"Eleazer, it is a good thing for you that I am in chains right now," Justus states between clenched teeth.

"My friends, do not hold this against my brother, for he did not intend to harm me," I manage to say.

"Peter is right, Justus, we must respond as Jesus would and extend forgiveness and unconditional love to Eleazer. We must reach out to him instead of rejecting and accusing him," Laban says.

"Oh, just shut-up," Eleazer angrily responds.

Their voices fade into the darkness as I wipe my face on my filthy sleeve. Ever so carefully I run my hand over my leg. It is now swollen to more than twice its normal size and fresh blood seeps from the open wound.

Dearest Father and beloved King, I pray for my brother, Eleazer. I ask You to heal his heart and open his eyes to see You in truth. You, Jesus, are the only One who can touch his guilt-filled heart and set him free from his past. I pray for his family and for his neighbors to find peace and love, to find You. You are the only One who can bring healing to such devastated hearts, so Lord, I ask You to do what only You can do.

I can hear Laban and Justus praying, too.

Teach my fellow prisoners to love each other as You love us. Give them the grace to forgive and embrace each other even in their weakness. Help them resist their old ways that they might walk in love.

"Peter, how are you now?" Josiah asks.

"I will be fine soon enough," I answer.

"Peter, you should rest. Laban and Justus and I will pray for you while you do so. We will also continue to pray for Eleazer."

The pain is too great for me to do anything else. Without even responding, I close my eyes. The last thing I remember is Eleazer mumbling something about not needing their prayers.

From the depths of my agony-filled sleep, I hear the sound of singing. Soft, beautiful, angelic singing.

Have I died? Am I in heaven? If so, then where is my beloved Savior and King?

"Peter, wake up. It is I, Miriam."

Miriam?

"Peter, I am here. Wake up, my love."

"Miriam?" I manage to whisper.

"Peter, it is I. Open your eyes, and look at me. Peter, let me know that you are well."

With great effort, I force myself out of the deep darkness that threatens to take me away. I try desperately, but unsuccessfully to open my eyes. "Is it really you or am I dreaming?" I ask, my voice hoarse from the raging fever and lack of water.

"It really is me, Peter. Are you going to spend the short time we have together sleeping? Wake up, my love."

I try to laugh, but that part of my body is not functioning.

I finally manage to open my eyes just enough to see Miriam kneeling beside me, her face just inches away from mine. "Are you real?" I ask through the fog that clouds my mind.

"You are not dreaming, my love, and I am very real. Your friends have told me that your leg is broken and that you were whipped. You also have a desperately high fever, my love."

I respond, "Both of those things are true, but let us not waste our precious time talking of such things."

I attempt to lift my head, but quickly discover that it is much too heavy.

Taking my bony hand in her bony hand, Miriam says, "Simon Peter, you have such a gift for getting yourself into difficult situations."

"It is for a good cause, is it not?" I ask.

"It is indeed," she responds while stroking my forehead.

"Tell me, how are you?" I ask once more trying to lift my head.

"I am well cared for, my love. And my heart still burns with uncompromising affection for our faithful and merciful King."

In the dim light, I can see that my wife is almost as thin as a blade of grass, but her countenance is brighter than those of a child seeing her first baby bird hatch.

"You look beautiful," I say.

"You look terrible," she replies.

"Well, I must admit that I have felt better," I respond forcing myself to smile. "I still have the lock of hair you sent me. I wound it around my little finger." I hold up my trembling hand for her to see.

She gently traces the frazzled hair and says, "I am forever grateful to you for choosing to follow the Master."

"That was the best decision I ever made, and the second best was marrying you," I reply.

"You are as kind as ever, my husband. And I would have to say that the day I gave my everything to Jesus was the greatest day of my life, and the second greatest day was when I became your wife."

"Miriam, come close."

She leans her beautiful face close to mine and I whisper, "I do not know how long I can go on. My body is failing me. My leg is badly broken and most certainly infected."

"But your spirit is stronger than ever, and Jesus is more than able to heal your body. Peter, I believe that there is still more for you to do on this earth."

I reply, "Miriam, that may be true, but I so long to be with Jesus again. I long to hear Him laugh, to see His face, to hear His voice and to see that delighted look that He always got when He looked at us.

"Miriam, I miss Him, and I am weary of this earth and all of its troubles."

"I miss Him, too. But do you remember, Peter, when Jesus told us that in this life we would have troubles, but not to be afraid, for He had overcome the world?"

"I remember, but that doesn't make it any easier," I respond.

"But it does give us hope, my love."

"It does indeed. We will see Him soon. And when we do, it will be absolutely glorious," I answer.

Miriam wipes my sweaty forehead with her tattered sleeve and then wipes the tears pooling in the corner of my eyes.

"How long can you stay?" I ask.

"Until Malchus returns, which will be sooner than either of us would like."

"I have missed you and never cease praying for you," I say looking into her beautiful dark brown eyes.

"I have missed you more than I can say," she says as she gently strokes my face. "Peter, I hear that you have led all your fellow prisoners to Christ, save one."

"By the grace of God. Have you met our Jewish brother, Eleazer?"

"I did, and he quickly informed me of his position concerning Jesus. I will join you in praying for his salvation. But, for now, allow me to pray for you. Perhaps, Jesus will mend your broken leg and heal your body of this fever as He healed my mother so many years ago. Do you remember that day, Peter?"

"How could I ever forget it?"

"It was the beginning of quite a journey. A journey that has taught us to love our enemies and to do good to those who despitefully use us. A journey where we have learned to not love our lives even unto death. Peter, it has been difficult, but ever so rewarding."

"Miriam, I believe this is the sickest I have ever been. I don't know if I will recover from this one."

"Nothing is too difficult for Jesus," Miriam softly replies and then lifts her voice in worship. Tears run down her face. Weak and completely exhausted, I close my eyes and listen to the wonderful sound of her voice as she sings:

> Lift up your heads, O gates,
> and be lifted up, O ancient doors,
> That the King of glory may come in!
> Who is the King of glory?
> The LORD strong and mighty,
> The LORD mighty in battle.
> Lift up your heads, O gates,
> And lift them up, O ancient doors,
> That the King of glory may come in!
> Who is this King of glory?
> The LORD of hosts,
> He is the King of glory.[17]

Strength pours through my body as the presence of the Lord surrounds me. Within minutes, I am completely lost in His wonderful, loving embrace. Joy floods my soul.

Miriam says, "Peter, one night sitting around the campfire, I asked Jesus for a gift, a gift that I have spent my entire life diligently seeking."

"What was it that you asked Him for?"

"I asked Him to give me a heart like David. I asked to be able to behold His beauty and meditate in His temple all the days of my life.[18]

"I have done that, my husband, and you have helped me to do so. We have lived our lives, by the grace of God, for the King. We have seen His beauty over and over again. We have seen it in the faces of the poor, our fellow prisoners and the guards. We have seen it in the eyes of those who are suffering and in so many other ways. And I have discovered that, in this prison, I have gained a revelation of Jesus that I would not have found in any other place.

"I have come to realize that His incomparable beauty lies in the depths of His great sacrifice and suffering. It is His scars, the marks on His body and His many sacrifices that makes Him so attractive to the human heart. He was despised and forsaken of men, a Man of sorrows, and acquainted with grief. He was despised, and no one esteemed Him. Surely our sicknesses He Himself bore, and our sorrows He carried with Him to the cross. He was pierced through for our transgressions; He was crushed for our iniquities. For our well-being, He took our punishment upon Himself, and by His scourging we are healed.[19]

"Peter, in the authority of Jesus, the King of the Jews and the Gentiles, in light of the fact that He carried your sickness in His body on the cross, I speak healing to you in His name, this same Jesus who will one day return to rule and reign over His Kingdom in the new Jerusalem. Peter, it is time to get out of the boat and walk on the water again."[20]

Healing power surges through my body like water rushing through a dam. The room spins once again, but this time it is delightful and exhilarating. Strength flows into and through me.

I carefully and slowly straighten my broken leg and feel no pain. Excited, I bend it back and forth and find that it is completely and absolutely free from pain!

"Glory to the Lamb!" I exclaim as I sit straight up and

embrace my wife. "Jesus has healed me! My leg is no longer broken, and my fever is gone! Oh, how I praise the Lord—He has completely healed me!"

Justus, Josiah and Laban quickly join our celebration. We have to keep reminding each other to be quiet, which is difficult considering the extent of our joy.

I look into my wife's tear-filled eyes and whisper, "You are altogether lovely, my sister, my bride."[21]

"You speak the words of king Solomon to me," she replies as she runs the back of her hand over my cheek.

"Did not the Lord say for husbands to love their wives in the same way He loves the church, which is His eternal partner like unto a bride?"[22]

"Yes, that is what He said."

"Well, my love, I am merely loving you the way Jesus loves you and saying what He would say to you if He were here."

"Oh, how I long for that day, Peter!"

"So do I, my love, so do I."

We hold each other. I have never been so grateful for my freedom from the chains as I am now.

"This may be the last time I see you on this earth," Miriam says.

"That is a very real possibility, but remember, my love, that this is not the end. When we die, it will just be the beginning of the most glorious adventure and unending journey of our entire lives. This life is our training ground and has a great deal to do with our eternal destiny. Therefore, it is most important how we live our lives. It is imperative that we are faithful not just in the large things, but also in the small things. And it is most crucial that we remain true to the end."

The prison door creaks open, and Malchus quietly enters. He says, "I am sorry, Peter, but it is time for Miriam to go."

With a kiss, she leaves my arms. I stand and, to my surprise, find that both of my legs are now perfectly straight and strong, but my joy is only momentary, for my heart is being ripped apart at the thought of Miriam's leaving.

I wonder if this is how Jesus felt when He had to leave us? I remember the look in His eyes when He told us that He was going to die. He then went on to say that He had to go so that He could send the Holy Spirit to us. At that time, I did not understand why He had to leave. Later, I came to realize that Jesus had to leave because He had a physical body, which could only be at one place at a time. But, the Holy Spirit would take up residence in every believer across the earth.[23]

Malchus suddenly exclaims, "Peter! Your leg! You are standing! I thank God for healing you!"

"I praise the Lord with you, my friend. And thank you for bringing my wife to visit me. You gave me a gift that I will treasure for as long as I live."

"I am grateful to the Lord for making it possible. Without His help and divine intervention, it would never have happened."

Holding Miriam ever so gently, I whisper to her, "Regardless of what comes your way, my love, always remember the Lord."

"How could I ever forget the One who gave His life to set me free, who became a criminal in my place, who loves me even in my weakness? I could never forget my King and my eternal Husband, just as I could never forget you, Peter."

"Go in peace, my love," I say as she steps out of my arms.

Picking up the small lamp, she addresses my fellow prisoners saying, "Do not worry about anything. Instead, pray about everything, giving thanks for all things, both good and bad. And the peace of God, which surpasses all comprehension, will guard your hearts and your minds in Christ Jesus.

"Fix your mind on whatever is true, whatever is honorable, whatever is right, whatever is pure, whatever is lovely, whatever is of good repute. Let your mind dwell on those things that are excellent and worthy of praise. [24]

"Since we have such a great cloud of witnesses surrounding us, let us also lay aside every weight and the sin which so easily entangles us, and let us run with endurance the race that is set before us. Fix your eyes on Jesus the author and perfecter of faith, who for the joy set before Him endured the cross, despising the shame. This same Jesus now sits at the right hand of the throne of God. Consider, my friends, this Jesus who endured great hostility at the hand of sinners against Himself, so that you may not grow weary and lose heart.[25] And hold fast, my fellow believers, to what you have in order that no one take your crown."[26]

With a smile, my precious wife turns to follow Malchus, but I know that she is really following the King, joyfully accepting His will for her life even if it means death.

With the closing of the door, I fall into a heap on the cold stone floor and weep for love, I weep for joy and for death that brings forth life eternal.

Oh, my God and King, You have given me gifts and graces that I do not deserve and could never earn! You are not only my Savior, but my Physician and Protector! You are so good to me! Thank You for Your never ending love! I am forever grateful to You for all that You have done!

Once my tears have ceased, Eleazer is the first to speak. "Peter, I just want to tell you how sorry I am that I kicked your leg. I really didn't mean to do that."

"Eleazer, I accept your apology and forgive you, my brother and my friend."

He responds, "I also want to say that your wife appears

to be very special. It is truly amazing that she has endured this awful place while maintaining such a tender, caring heart."

"Miriam is a very special lady, and it is a great joy to me that she loves Jesus enough to suffer for Him."

As I feel my way around our dark cell, Josiah adds, "I was very impacted by her humility and her love for Jesus and her concern for us. She even inquired as to our physical and spiritual condition before she tried to wake you, Peter."

"And I was impacted by the way she has maintained a close relationship with Jesus even though He has not opened the prison doors and set her free," Laban states.

Justus adds, "I was most impacted by the purity of her heart. It was obvious that she really cares for people. I also loved the fact that God flowed through her to heal your body, Peter. That was so wonderful!"

"Everything that you say is true, my friends. My wife is a masterpiece, for God took a chunk of coal and fashioned a stunning diamond, which is exactly what He does for all of us, if we allow Him."

"But can He do that in the short time we have left?" Justus asks.

"Nothing is impossible for God."

"Is your wife going to die at the hands of Nero, Peter?" Eleazer asks.

"My wife is ready to meet her Lord and King face to face. And, on that day, I am certain she will hear those words we all long to hear, 'Well done, my good and faithful servant, enter into your place of rest.'"[27]

"Peter, I hope I'm not being selfish in asking, but I am aching to hear more about your time with Jesus," Justus says.

"As am I," Laban adds.

"Me, too," Josiah states.

"Then, let us do as Miriam encouraged and fix our eyes

on Jesus the author and perfecter of our faith," I say with renewed strength.[28]

I quickly whisper a prayer, "Oh, how wonderful You are—not just because You healed me, but because You so completely love weak human beings like me."

CHAPTER SIX

After leaving the Gadarenes we crossed over to the other side of the lake where we were met by a large crowd. Several men hurried out into the water and pulled our boat to shore.

Leaping out of the boat with ease, Jesus warmly greeted the people. By their enthusiastic response, it was obvious that they were glad to see Him. Ignoring their praises, Jesus hurried through the midst of them toward a boy who could not have been more than six years of age. The sad looking lad sat on a nearby rock, completely alone.

After a few moments of conversation, Jesus scooped up the little guy in His arms and said, "Samuel, you are healed."[29]

The little boy's eyes suddenly grew wide and his mouth fell open. Throwing his arms around Jesus' neck, he exclaimed, "Is it true? Am I to walk? Am I to run and play just like the other boys?"

Jesus gently laughed. Hugging him tightly, He answered, "Yes, Samuel, it is true. You can now run and play just like all the other boys."

"Please, would you set me down that I might try out my new legs?"

"Certainly," Jesus responded and placed him on his feet.

At first, Samuel remained motionless, but that lasted for only a moment. With his hand tightly clutching Jesus' hand, he took a step and then another and another.

A young woman suddenly pushed me out of the way. Rushing past me, I heard her say, "That's my son!"

When she was a few feet away from the little boy, she came to an abrupt halt. Her hand flew to her mouth, and she fell to her knees. Tears streamed down her face. Samuel looked up, and upon seeing his mother, he quickly let go of Jesus' hand and ran with arms outstretched into her waiting embrace.

The two laughed and cried at the same time as she hugged him tightly. Pushing back from her, the little boy said, "Mother, Jesus has healed me!"

"I can see that," she answered and stood to her feet. Overjoyed, she spun her little boy around. Dizzy, the two fell to the ground. Brushing the hair back from his mother's face, Samuel said, "Now I can play just like the other boys! Now I can help you carry the water and pick the grapes and chase the chickens and do all sorts of things that little boys should do!"

"Samuel, I don't know what to say!" she replied.

Leaning close to his mother's ear, Samuel said, "Just say, 'Thank you.' " And he pointed to Jesus.

Standing, the young woman reached down to carry her son, but he quickly reminded her that it was no longer necessary to do so. Hand in hand the two walked toward Jesus. With fresh tears rolling down her face, Samuel's mother said, "Thank You for healing my little boy. I am forever in your debt, kind Sir."

Jesus laid His hand on Samuel's head and responded,

"Everyone who asks, receives; and he who seeks, finds; and to him who knocks, it shall be opened."[30]

"Who are you?" she asked.

"Who am I? I am gentle and humble of heart," He answered.[31]

Samuel tugged on his mother's tunic, saying, "Mother, can we go home now? I want to show everyone what I can do."

"Sure, Samuel," she responded without taking her eyes off of Jesus.

Samuel pulled on his mother's tunic. She slowly and reluctantly followed.

Jesus turned to the crowd and said, "Come to Me, all who are weary and heavy-laden, and I will give you rest. Take My yoke upon you, and learn from Me, for I am gentle and humble in heart; and you shall find rest for your souls, for My yoke is easy, and My load is light."[32]

Samuel's mother stopped to listen.

Hearing someone shouting Jesus' name, I turned around. Jairus, the ruler of the synagogue, frantically pushed his way through the crowd. The people resisted him until they saw who it was that so desperately pursued the Master.

Because of his position as ruler of the synagogue, Jairus is one of the most important and respected men in the community. So, why would someone of his reputation be seeking Jesus?

After much effort, Jairus finally stood before Jesus but only for a moment. Within seconds, he fell to his knees and cried out, "My little daughter is at the point of death! Please, come and lay Your hands on her that she might live and not die!"

Jesus reached down and raised Jairus up, saying, "I will go with you."

A look of relief and faint hope softened the panicked

look in Jairus's eyes. Without any hesitation, he clutched Jesus' extended hand and stood to his feet. Without letting go of Jesus' hand, Jairus quickly led the way shouting, "Make way; make way for the Teacher!"

I am shocked that Jairus has humbled himself to such a degree by coming to the Master. I would have thought that he, like most of the other religious leaders, consider Jesus to be a heretic, a dangerous outsider. He must love his daughter very much to risk their criticism and possible rejection.

With Jairus leading the way, the people standing along the streets pointed in wonder. They, too, were shocked to see someone of Jairus's stature with a lowly Man like Jesus. Curious, many of them joined the already large following. Jesus was pressed against on every side to the point that He could barely walk.

Looking at John, I shouted over the noise of the crowd, "At this rate, it will be the Feast of Tabernacles before we get to Jairus's house!"

Abruptly, Jesus stopped. He turned around and shouted, "Who touched Me?"

I looked at James and John who simply shrugged. Leaning forward, I said to Jesus, "You see the people pressing in on You on every side; and still You ask, 'Who touched Me?'"

He did not respond, but continued searching the crowd. Jairus's eyes were filled with pain and agony as he nervously rocked from foot to foot. He was anxious for the Master to resume the journey to his daughter's side.

It appears that Jesus is not going anywhere until He identifies this mysterious one who touched Him, but why? What reason could He have for identifying the culprit?

He looked to His left and then took a few steps forward; the crowd parted before Him. I looked at the object of His gaze. Crouched behind a very large man was a small and obviously frightened woman. She saw the Master looking at her, and her countenance fell like an apple falls from a tree. Her thin, fragile frame trembled before Him.

The woman fell headlong at the Master's feet and blurted out, "Teacher, I have had a hemorrhage for twelve years and have suffered greatly at the hand of many physicians, which cost me all that I have. I did everything the doctors instructed but have only grown worse."

Hearing her confession, the crowd moved away as though she had leprosy.

This woman is unclean! How dare she break the Law by coming out in public!

Undaunted by their response, she continued, "I followed You today knowing that You were my only hope, for I was told that You have the power to heal. I believed that if I could only touch the hem of Your garment, I would be made well. So, I ignored the Law, which strictly forbids me to touch anyone because of the condition I was in and pushed my way through this great crowd in order to reach You.

"I am the one who touched You. And it is true what I believed, for I was healed the moment my fingers touched the tassel on the hem of Your garment."

She reached out once again and lovingly touched the blue and white tassel.

How could anyone be healed by just touching the fringe on the Master's garment?

Jesus reached down and took her frail hand in His strong one and raised her up. With a smile, He said, "Daughter, it was not the hem of My garment that healed you; it was your faith in your Savior who healed you. Go in peace."

The woman, with the largest of smiles and head held high, thanked the Master several times and then quickly disappeared into the crowd. With an exclamation of joy,

Jesus put His arm around Jairus's shoulder and said, "Now, let us go to your daughter's side."

Without any hesitation, Jairus once again led the way. We had gone only a short distance when a frantic-looking servant broke through the crowd and whispered something to Jairus. Immediately, the color drained from his face. Choking back the tears, he turned to Jesus and said, "It is too late—my daughter is dead!"

Jairus collapsed on the ground. Jesus knelt beside him and laid His hand on Jairus' shoulder. The two men simply stared at each other. Jairus' eyes were filled with excruciating pain while Jesus' eyes were filled with great love and tender compassion.

Like a drowning man, Jairus clutched Jesus' arm. His tears fell on the Master's sleeve. Jairus groaned deeply crying out, "Jesus!"

A man from the crowd shouted, "Why do you bother the Teacher? It is too late, for your child is already dead." The woman standing beside the man elbowed him.

Jesus laid His hand on Jairus' white knuckles and said, "Do not be afraid that My coming will be of no purpose, only believe and your daughter shall be made well."

Only believe? Only believe what?

Time stood still as Jairus stared into an endless well of compassion clothed in frail humanity. Finally, with the slightest of nods and the weakest of whispers, Jairus took the Master's hand once more. The two men stood to their feet and the crowd parted like the Red Sea. Many followed after them eager to see what would happen next.

We struggled to keep up with Jairus, for he was a desperate man. I could not help but think of the excruciating pain that awaited him. I found myself dreading what was to come.

I cannot imagine what it would be like to return home and find that your child was dead.

Without stopping, we traveled the rough, dusty roads. The sun was cloaked with thick, dark clouds as though heaven joined this father in mourning.

It was not long before his house came into sight. At which point, Jairus could no longer contain his grief; his loud wailing filled the countryside. Tears filled my eyes.

Oh, how he loved his daughter!

I tried to make my way to Jesus' side but could not because the crowd was too great.

As soon as we stepped into Jairus's spacious courtyard, we heard the wailing of the flutes and the loud lamenting of the mourners.

Jairus rent his garment from top to bottom and then ran into his home. Jesus instructed the crowd to remain outside and told James, John and myself to follow.

The house and everyone in it was in extreme chaos. Relatives, hired mourners, wailing women and musicians filled the place. Jesus followed Jairus into the room where the little girl was laid. With fear and trepidation, the three of us followed.

Being in the presence of a dead person is not something Jewish people do.

According to our Jewish custom, professional mourners were bent over the girl's body, begging for a response. Other hired mourners lined the walls, rocking back and forth on their knees as they shrieked, beat their breasts and pulled on their hair.

Standing just inside the doorway, surveying the scene, Jesus shouted, "Why is everyone weeping? The child isn't dead; she's merely asleep!"

The shrieking of the women stopped, the wailing of the flutes faded, and the entreaties directed at the corpse ceased. Every eye turned to look at the Man who would be so foolish as to say such a ridiculous thing.

It started first as a chuckle and then quickly escalated

to laughter followed by mocking. Ignoring their response, Jesus simply ushered them out of the room, leaving only Jairus, James, John and myself in the room with the dead body. I stepped back against the wall.

It is much too quiet in here.

To my relief, Jesus returned quickly and said, "There is no need for mourners in this home."

What does Jesus mean? Of course we need mourners—it is our custom.

Jairus stared at his only daughter who was laid on a low table in the center of the room. She looked to have been about twelve years old. What a beautiful girl she was! Her complexion was as smooth as the sea on a windless day. A garland of wildflowers had been placed on her head. Her long, black hair was perfectly draped over her shoulders. Her delicate, snow-white hands lay folded over her motionless heart. It was obvious from her purple lips and from her skin, which was whiter than a newly washed lamb, that this little girl had been dead for quite some time.

Jairus stood over his lovely daughter, speechless and unmoving. The room was painfully quiet, as quiet as this little girl's body.

Why are we here?

Suddenly, the door flew open causing me to nearly jump out of my skin. A woman, dressed in black, rushed into the room. Without saying a word or even acknowledging that anyone was there, she threw herself on her knees and scooped up the child in her arms.

Her cries are nothing like those of the paid mourners; these cries come from a shattered heart. She is most certainly the child's mother.

She rocked back and forth, moaning and groaning all the while.

She did not acknowledge Jairus's presence until he

laid his hand on her shoulder. Looking up, she said, "Jairus, you must do something!"

"Oh, to be able to turn the world upside down and make wrong things right! Oh, how I wish I could give her life! What good is money, power or status when the object of your affection slips from your hand like water runs through your fingers?" he agonized.

The child's mother resumed her violent rocking as though the motion would start her heart beating again.

I know that she is distraught, but to embrace a corpse is the most defiling kind of uncleanness there is. This woman must be out of her mind with grief!

Jesus laid His hand on my shoulder startling me.

Just one glance His way, and I can clearly see the error of my ways. Of course, this mother is holding her daughter! Why do I always put the traditions of the Elders before the needs of people?

With a reassuring nod my way, Jesus stepped behind Jairus who was now kneeling beside his wife and whispering words that I could not hear. Jairus took his daughter's small hand into his large one and kissed each one of her fingers. His tears fell like rain.

The Master looked on with great compassion.

Perhaps, the reason He has brought us here is to offer comfort to this distraught family.

Jesus stepped around to the other side of the table and knelt. The girl's parents did not seem to notice until Jesus took one of her limp hands in His and spoke tenderly and gently, but with great authority in the Aramaic language, saying, "Talitha cumi," which means, "Little girl, arise!"

Immediately, the dead girl inhaled deeply. Her skin quickly regained its olive color, and her lips turned red. The child's mother fell backwards, dropping her back on the table. The little girl opened her eyes and sat straight up. Looking at her speechless father, she waved. Her smile was more than her parents could take. They both shrieked as they embraced her, covering her with kisses and tears. After thoroughly lavishing her with their great affection, they looked at Jesus who smiled and said, "Now, give her something to eat."

Perplexed, Jairus looked at his wife as though Jesus had spoken a foreign language and whispered, "Do you think it's safe to let her eat so soon after—after being dead?"

The girl's mother replied, "Well, dear, I can't say that I know the answer to that question since I've never met a dead person who came back to life."

She then began to laugh, softly at first, and then with great abandonment. Her laughter was contagious and soon we were all laughing. And all the while, the little girl seemed completely unaware that anything spectacular had happened.

Jesus laid His hand on Jairus' shoulder and said, "Tell no one what has happened here."

Jairus slowly nodded, too happy, too stunned, too amazed to do anything more.

"And, don't forget to give her something to eat," Jesus added chuckling.[33]

This maiden was dead—there's no doubt about that. But now she lives, she talks, she walks and can eat! How did Jesus do this?

The little girl suddenly jumped up from the table where only moments ago she lay dead. Standing on her tiptoes, she removed the garland of flowers from her head and placed it on Jesus' head. With the sweetest and most innocent of smiles, she said, "I crown You King of the universe!"

At that precise moment, beams of sunlight streamed in through the open window and covered Jesus' face with golden light.

Leaning over to John, I whispered, "Heaven seems to agree with the child."

"Indeed," he answered.

CHAPTER SEVEN

Laban states, "I would have loved to see Jesus raise that girl from the dead."

"Who's to say that she was really dead?" Eleazer mumbles under his breath.

"I saw her with my own eyes, my friend, and she was most certainly dead. For as long as I live, however short that may be, I will never forget the moment when her still, lifeless body drew that first breath. It was quite extraordinary and very terrible at the same time."

Eleazer grunts loudly.

Ignoring him, I continue, "The Creator of mankind is more than able to raise the dead, my friend."

"Peter," Josiah says, "Jesus did the same thing for me. I was dead in my sins, condemned to die when Jesus invited me into His Kingdom, granting me eternal life. Just as surely as He restored life to that little girl, He restored life to me. The only difference was that I was a walking dead man and didn't know it. I was headed straight for the fires of hell, but now I am forgiven and headed straight for the arms of Jesus," Josiah adds.

"Only God can forgive sins," Eleazer mutters loud enough for all to hear.

"That is a true statement, my brother—only God can forgive sins. Which brings us to the real question—is Jesus the Son of God? Is He the Messiah?

"If He is, then you have a serious problem. Believe me, brother, this is a question that you most certainly want to know the answer to before you die, for it determines where you will spend eternity. Knowing the answer to that question is worth any price, any effort that you have to make, because eternity is forever and Satan is a ruthless, merciless jailor— much worse than any of the guards in this prison. There is an eternal prison, my friend, where demons torment their prisoners, and, in comparison, this place will seem like a picnic."

"And none of us have any time to waste," Laban adds.

"Speaking of time," Justus says, "I would really like to know what Jesus did after raising that girl from the dead."

"And I would really like to tell you, but I think someone is coming," I answer.

We wait in silence as the distant sound of footsteps grows closer. I hear Brutus cursing, and dread fills me.

O Lord, You are our refuge, our portion in the land of the living. Give heed to our cry, for we are brought very low; deliver us from our persecutors, for they are too strong for us![34]

The door swings open with its usual groans and creaks. Brutus thrusts his torch in my face saying, "I am the light and in me is no darkness!"

"You quote the Lord," I say trying desperately to shield my eyes.

"I quote the one you call lord, but to me he is nothing more than a bad dream. Speaking of bad dreams," he says grabbing me by the hair of my head, "I am your worst nightmare."

With a jerk, he drags me across the floor. "I thought you'd be dead by now. I can't tell you how overjoyed I am to find that you are still alive. I bet you didn't know that you are my favorite prisoner. I would miss you terribly should something tragic happen to you. I would be so bored if I didn't have you to torment, for you have been quite a challenge for me."

How much can I endure, Lord? Give me grace and strength needed to remain faithful to you!

"You are a piece of trash, a pile of dung, a scum of a man!" he says.

He abruptly drops me on the floor just outside my cell. "I have missed our times together, Simon Peter. Come now, have you nothing to say?"

"I have only one thing to say, and that is the truth: Jesus Christ died for you because He loves you!"

In a flash, the back of his hand lands squarely across my mouth. "No one has ever died *for* me! They may have died *on account of me*, but not *for* me!" he says laughing loudly.

"You are sadly mistaken, Brutus. There is One who died for you, and His name is Jesus," I say as blood runs down my chin and onto my neck.

"Enough of your foolish talk! It's time to get down to business."

I hear the sound of the whip and cringe. I count nine lashes before I pass out. I am immediately surrounded by the most glorious light imaginable. The sound of distant singing reminds me of my wife; I have always loved the sound of her voice. A movement to my left captures my attention. There, standing before me is my beloved King! I run to Him, falling prostrate at His feet. I suddenly realize that my mouth is no longer bleeding and my body is free from all pain.

"Jesus, I love You, and I will follow hard after You for

as long as I live!" I shout.

"Peter, *I* am the light of the world and in *Me* is no darkness! I am your Shepherd; therefore, you shall not want. I make you lie down in green pastures. I lead you beside quiet waters. I restore your soul. I guide you in the paths of righteousness for the sake of My name. Even though you walk through the valley of the shadow of death, you shall fear no evil because I am with you. Do you hear Me, Peter? I am with you! I will never leave you, Peter!"

I nod, saying, "I know that You will never leave me nor forsake me."

"My rod and My staff comfort you, and I prepare a table before you in the presence of your enemies. I have anointed your head with oil; your cup overflows. Surely goodness and mercy will follow you all the days of your life. And you, Peter, will surely dwell in My house forever."[35]

"Lord, how much longer before I am with You?" I ask.

"Peter, I am with you even now, My friend. I am with you. I am with you. Do you hear Me, Peter, I am with you, even now...."

His voice fades away as I return to consciousness and the brutal whip ripping through my flesh. With each lash, I thank the Lord for the stripes He bore for me.

Exhausted, Brutus finally stops. He then orders a guard to drag me back into my cell where I am thrown on the floor and left in a bloody heap. I rejoice that it is over. My back, arms and chest feel as though thousands of hot needles are sticking in me. I feel very ill.

Lord, is there no end to this senseless torture?

I hear the still, small voice of God answer, "Peter, your devotion has conquered My heart."

But, Lord, I am growing weary. How can I go on?

"Is any among you suffering? Let him pray.[36] To the degree that you share My sufferings, keep on rejoicing because there will be a day when I will make wrong things right," He whispers within my heart.[37]

How long, Lord? How long before it comes to an end?

"Love me to the end, Peter; love Me to the end. Blessed is the man who perseveres under trial; for once he has been approved, he will receive a crown of life, which is promised to those who love Me."[38]

Help me, Lord.

"Peter, in My darkest hour, I fought for you."

When was Your darkest hour, Lord?

"When I hung on Calvary's hill, for it was there that I took on the sins of the entire world. It was there that My Father forsook Me as I embraced sin. It was there that I conquered your enemy once and for all time. Satan is a conquered foe, My friend, so persevere, Peter, for I came to give you life."

I, too, will pay the price in this, my darkest hour.

"I will love and be with you to the end, My friend," He says as He reaches through the veil that separates the eternal from the temporal. Suddenly, grace, beautiful grace, floods my being. He whispers, "My grace will see you through, Peter. It is more than enough to see you through."

"Peter, is there anything I can do for you?" Josiah asks, unknowingly interrupting my glorious encounter.

"The greatest thing that one soul can do for another is pray for them," I answer.

"I can certainly do that," Josiah answers.

Laying on the cold stone floor, I thank God that they did not chain me. "I need to sleep, my friends. Wake me in a little while," I say.

Exhausted, I fall asleep to the sound of Josiah's prayers. My sleep is anything but restful, for it is filled with wave after wave of searing, hot pain. Unbearable burning and throbbing wake me. I try to restrain from groaning, but find it impossible.

"Peter?"

77

"Yes, Josiah," I respond.

"Perhaps, Jesus will heal your body just as He healed your leg. What do you think?"

"I think that one should always ask, my friend."

"Laban, Justus, Eleazer—would you join with me in asking Jesus to touch our brother's broken body?" Josiah asks.

Eleazer grunts, but Laban and Justus heartily agree.

I close my eyes.

O Lord, please grant our requests and use it to capture Eleazer's heart.

Through my closed eyelids, I see a small light, which quickly becomes larger and brighter. From within the light, a hand is extended holding a shepherd's staff. I reach up and take hold of it, and something like pure, liquid love flows through it and into my body. It is so intense that it is almost painful, and yet it so glorious that I do not want to let it go. A voice speaks, "I am the same yesterday, today and forever!"[39]

I respond, "Lord, I count all things to be loss in view of the surpassing value of knowing You. I have suffered the loss of all things for Your sake, and I count all things to be rubbish that I might be found in You. My righteousness does not come from the Law, but my righteousness comes through faith in You.

"Oh, dear Lord, I long to know You and the power of Your resurrection and the fellowship of Your sufferings, being conformed to Your death."[40]

"Will you dare to believe that My love is greater than your weakness?" Jesus asks.

"Give me the grace to believe, Lord."

He responds, "Love never fails." Healing power surges throughout my body. I sit quietly for a moment, whispering a prayer of thanksgiving.

Sitting up, I exclaim, "Give thanks to the Lord for He

has touched me again, and I am healed!"

Jumping to my feet, I dance around in the darkness. No one says anything until I have thoroughly exhausted myself, which does not take very long considering my weak physical condition.

"It cannot be true. I cannot believe that this is true," Eleazer says as if talking to himself.

"My dear brother, it is true, and you can know this same healing power in your life. Your sins can be forgiven, your soul can be free, and your heart can be healed."

"You don't know what you are saying. That is impossible, for I have lived a life of sin; I don't deserve anything other than punishment. If there is a God, and what you say is true, then I, more than anyone, deserve to spend eternity in hell," he responds.

"My brother, we all deserve hell, but thank God for His infinite love that made a way for all to be rescued from such a fate. Do not allow your pride or self- righteousness to cause you to delay any longer, for you do not know the hour when you will meet the Lord face to face. He is offering you a free gift, one that He paid a dear price to give you; it is the gift of salvation. Will you come to Him just as you are and receive His free gift of forgiveness and eternal life?"

"I cannot do what you say, for you have not convinced me."

"It is not my responsibility to convince you, Eleazer. That is between you and your Maker."

"Then tell me more, Peter. Tell me stories of your Savior that will crush my stony heart. Kill me with words of life, Peter, and do not hold back! Assault me with the truth and drive me to my knees! Perhaps, this God of yours will have mercy on me and open my ears that I might hear and believe. If this Jesus is who you say he is, I ask that he would shatter me now that I might be spared his wrath on the day I stand before him! Oh, that he would come and kill me, and put me out of my misery!"

"It is the kindness of God that leads men to repentance, Eleazer."[41]

"Then kill me with kindness! Kill me with words of life! Throw your net and capture me, Peter, for I am a prisoner of this evil world and I know it! Do what I cannot do— break through my defenses and tear down the lies that I believe! Rip my heart out with words of life, flood my soul with truth! Overwhelm me with kindness!"

"You can be free. You can know peace. You can live, Eleazer," I respond.

"Convince me, Peter, and I will believe," he says, sounding like a man who has given up.

"Eleazer, you shall know the truth and the truth will set you free. So, listen my friend to the greatest story ever told," I answer.

CHAPTER EIGHT

After Jesus restored life to Jairus's daughter, we returned to Capernaum. As we approached the city, we came upon a group of men sitting by the road. Among them were two blind men. Hearing our approach, they held out their beggar's cups, which were nothing more than pieces of broken pottery. Hearing Jesus' name, the blind men scrambled to their feet, but Jesus kept going without so much as a glance there way. Suddenly, one of the blind men shouted out, "Son of David! Have pity on us!"

Jesus walked on. Undaunted, the men followed us into the city, proclaiming all along the way that the Messiah had come and His name was Jesus.

How is it that these men, who have no natural sight can see spiritual things so clearly? How is it that they are able to see the great things of God, which are hidden from the wise and prudent?

Jesus seemed to be ignoring them, but they were not discouraged. On the contrary, they cried out even more saying, "Son of David, have mercy on us!"

We arrived at my house, and the two blind men followed

us inside still pleading with Jesus to heal them.

Jesus faced them and asked, "Do you believe that I have the power to do this?"

Without hesitation they replied, "Yes, Lord, we know that You can restore sight to the blind, that you can give us sight."

With a smile and a nod, Jesus reached out and touched their eyes saying, "Then let it happen to you according to your faith."

When He withdrew His hand, the wondrous expression on their faces revealed the truth—they both could see!

With a shout, they embraced each other and then danced a jig until falling into a heap on the floor. Chuckling, Jesus knelt beside them. The two men looked up into the eyes of a King, even though the rest of us did not see that He was anything more than a Rabbi with amazing power and remarkable authority.

"You did it! You healed us!"

"See that no one knows about this," He sternly warned them.

"But?" they responded.

Jesus repeated, "Tell no one about this miracle."

"Okay," they reluctantly replied. Like two young boys, they jumped to their feet and quickly ran out of my house.

Standing in the doorway, I watched as they ran down the streets proclaiming that Jesus had restored their sight. I looked at Jesus who seemed to be unaffected by their blatant disobedience.[42]

Why would they do exactly what He asked them not to do?

"Come, Simon," Jesus said, placing His hand on my shoulder.

I followed Jesus out the back door and through the field. He stopped under the shade of a large tree where we sat. I was the first to speak, "Those men received a wonderful gift from You, and they completely disregarded Your command to be silent about it. You don't seem angry about it in the least. How is that?"

"Simon, a disciple of Mine must embrace meekness. Each day, he must decide to live his life as a humble, gentle, loving servant because meekness is a magnet that attracts the favor of God."[43]

He paused allowing His words to penetrate my dull heart.

He is not troubled by this at all. He has not taken the role of victim, neither is He offended. He is at perfect peace.

"Peter, you only have a short time on this earth. Why not spend it by responding with unconditional love to those who dishonor, ignore, overlook or wrongly accuse you? Take every opportunity to esteem others as more important than yourself, for this is meekness.[44]

"Meekness is the opposite of pride. It is power under the restraint of love. Meekness means choosing to take the back seat, the low road. It means that you will serve those you feel should be serving you. It means that you will humble yourself and seek reconciliation even when you are the innocent party. It means that you must be willing to be seen as the guilty party so that you might win others."[45]

"What!? How can this be? Why should I be accused of being guilty when I am innocent? There is no justice in that!"

"At the end of the day, when it really matters, meekness always wins, Peter. Meekness endures the cross for the sake of the guilty, My friend. The Son of man did not come to be served but to serve," He said looking off into the distance.

"But I want justice!"

Jesus looked directly into my eyes, laid His hand on my shoulder and asked, "Do you really, Peter? Do you really want God to deal with you according to what you deserve?"

Conviction filled my soul.

Without waiting for a response, Jesus continued, "It is the kindness of God that leads men to repentance, Peter.[46] Believe Me, you are much better off having God respond to you according to His infinite lovingkindness—according to His mercies which are new every morning—than according to what you deserve."

"It is true that I would prefer that God deal with me according to mercy, but I also want to see justice when it comes to my dealings with man. Otherwise, I will be taken advantage of."

"Peter, in this life you will have troubles, that is certain. But have no fear, take courage; I have overcome the world.[47]

"You see, Peter, meekness is not based on justice neither is it based on what we think we deserve. Meekness is based on an unselfish life that is poured out for the benefit of others. Meekness, simply put, is the act of faithfully cultivating a servant's heart that seeks the best for others even at your own expense. Meekness is standing before your enemy, refusing to accuse, condemn or attack him. It is extending unconditional love to him. This kind of lifestyle will mean death to your desires and your flesh and death to your rights, but it results in life for all parties involved."

"Sounds pretty painful to me," I said kicking a rock.

"I didn't say it wouldn't be painful. Some of the most beautiful things on this earth are birthed through pain."

"How do I acquire this meekness?" I asked.

"Ask God to help you. Ask Him for the grace to walk in meekness. Make the decision to bless and serve those you come in contact with. Do not look for justice, but look for ways to walk in humility, esteeming others as greater than yourself and giving up your right to be right, especially when the other person is mostly wrong. Choose to be the one who initiates reconciliation, who does not point the finger, who does not stand on his rights, but takes the position of a humble servant. After all, a dead man has no rights, and you are dead men if you follow Me."[48]

"This sounds like a sure fire way to have people walk all over me," I respond.

"I am telling you that dying to your selfish way of living produces a fragrant, fruitful life, for God gives grace to the humble and opposes the proud, My friend."[49]

My heart sank.

How could I ever live like this? It is so contrary to my nature, to my desires.

"With God all things are possible," Jesus answered, knowing my thoughts.[50]

I looked up and saw that the crowds had discovered the Master's whereabouts and were descending upon us like vultures descending upon a dead animal.

"It is time, Peter," Jesus said.

"Don't you ever get tired of them?" I asked.

"Could an Artist grow tired of His masterpiece? Could a Musician ever grow tired of His music? Could a Father reject His children? Could God ever grow tired of the very object of His great affections?"

What passion! What fire! What devotion! What love! Just who is this Man?!

Affectionately slapping my back, He stood. "Let us go out to meet them."

Without wasting another minute, He hurried to them and immediately began teaching and healing the sick. While doing so, a man was brought to Jesus. He looked to be about thirty years old. He stood before Jesus with his head down and his shoulders drooping. Suddenly and quite unexpectedly, the man fell to his knees and looked up at Jesus. His eyes pleaded for help, and yet he said not a word.

I wonder what he wants.

An elderly man stepped forward and said, "Teacher, he cannot speak; he is mute."

With great compassion, Jesus placed His hand on the man's shoulder and commanded, "Come out of him!"

The man coughed. His face contorted for a brief moment, and then he let out a long, deep sigh. Within minutes, his eyes lit up. Opening his mouth, he proclaimed the goodness of God. The crowd, completely amazed, shouted, "Nothing like this has ever been seen in Israel!"

Jesus embraced the man who could not stop thanking the God of heaven for his deliverance. The crowd responded like a hive of bees that just got turned upside down. Everyone was trying get close enough to touch this Miracle Worker from Nazareth.

Jesus responded to their unbridled zeal and selfish motives with great tenderness. He embraced some while confronting others. It was amazing to watch Jesus speak the truth with so much love that the person being rebuked felt loved and valued.

Later in the day, Jesus continued on His way. As we followed, I meditated on His words about meekness.

Jesus perfectly portrays humility in every situation. He makes no demands for anyone to serve Him, not even His closest disciples, which is appropriate and even expected of a rabbi. He never despairs of the unending crowds. Neither does He fail to extend mercy to the most despicable of sinners. He never condemns anyone, but neither does He fail to speak the truth, speaking in such a way that brings conviction and exposes the hidden issues of the heart.

We had walked only a short distance when several Pharisees approached our traveling party. Stopping directly in front of Jesus, the eldest held up his hand and said, "It is through the ruler of the demons that you expel demons!"

Jesus looked deep into his eyes and then into the eyes

of the others. Within minutes, all of them either looked away or stared at the ground. He then stepped around them without saying a word, without defending Himself and walked on.[51]

Why didn't He defend Himself?

Jesus paused long enough to look at me. His eyes pierced my soul, and I remembered His words.

Of course! Once more Jesus responds with meekness! If that had been me, I would have set those men straight and won the battle.

"You might have won the battle, but you would have certainly lost the war," Jesus responded to my wrong thinking.

How quickly I forget.

Several days later, we left Capernaum and headed towards Jesus' hometown of Nazareth.

The last time He was there His fellow townspeople tried to throw Him off a cliff. This will certainly be interesting, to say the least.

We arrived in Nazareth just before the Sabbath. Of course Jesus went straight to the synagogue. Finding a group gathered, He began to teach. The people were clearly astonished by the depth of His wisdom and the clarity of insight that He shed on the Scriptures. They were also quite perplexed, and some were even offended at His messages.

After several hours, a man stood and asked, "Isn't this man a carpenter and the son of a carpenter? Don't we know his mother? Isn't he the brother of James, Joses, Judas and Simon? Do not his sisters live here?"

Another responded, "Indeed, this is the same Jesus who grew up with our children. His father was Joseph, the carpenter, and Mary is his mother."

Another jumped to his feet and asked, "Then, where did this man learn these things? What is this wisdom he has been given? And how do we explain the many reports we have received of great miracles that he has done?"

Another exclaimed, "He may appear to be gifted, and reports may be given, yet we know that he is nothing more than a carpenter and the son of a carpenter!"

Jesus responded to their accusations by saying, "A Prophet is without honor in His hometown, among His own relatives and in His own house."

He then walked out of the synagogue.

We did not stay many days in Nazareth because Jesus could do no miracles there other than heal a few sick people. As we stood on a hill just outside the city, Jesus stared down at His hometown for a long time. Shaking His head, He said, "I am amazed at their unbelief!"

This is the first time I have ever heard Jesus say that something amazed Him. Sad that it would be something so negative.

We followed Jesus through the surrounding towns and villages. He taught in their synagogues, proclaiming that the Kingdom had come. He healed every kind of disease and weakness.[52]

With the noon sun burning down on us, Jesus led His large following to an orchard where we could get a respite from the heat and rest. The crowd eagerly complied.

Leaning against a tree, Jesus watched the people as they wandered here and there. He whispered, "Look at them, Peter. They are like sheep without a shepherd. They wander here and there. They are weary and cannot find their way. Oh, how I love them! Oh, how I care for them!"

His eyes were two pools of liquid love with streams of compassion running unhindered down His sunburned face.

I looked across the sea of people and felt nothing, except maybe a bit of irritation. I looked at the other apostles; they were busy cracking walnuts seemingly oblivious to Jesus' statement of adoration.

What is it that He sees in mankind that moves Him to such depths of loving compassion?

With His head resting against the tree trunk, Jesus silently wept.

It's amazing that the most powerful Man I have ever met weeps over weak, frail human beings.

I scanned the multitude once again.

The people appear to be perfectly content, and yet Jesus obviously sees something that I cannot see and feels something that I cannot feel. I wonder what it is like to love like this? He has more compassion in His little finger than I do in my entire body.

After a lengthy rest, the great Shepherd led us on. As was His custom, He taught as He walked. There was no sign of the pain in His heart as He eagerly shared the good news of the Kingdom.

At the end of the day, we stopped beside a cornfield to camp for the night. As we stretched out under the glorious blanket of heaven, Jesus said, "The harvest is ready for reaping; it is plenteous, but the workers are few. Therefore, beseech the Lord of the harvest to send out workers to gather the harvest."[53]

Eager to please, I silently prayed, "God, would You send laborers to the man who owns this field? He must be in need of help."

"Peter," Jesus whispered, "you are delightful!"

CHAPTER NINE

Justus interrupts saying, "Peter, listen—someone is singing!"

In the distance, someone was indeed singing quite loudly.

Whoever it is must be Jewish because he is singing in perfect Hebrew.

As the voice grows closer, I recognize the song as one of king David's psalms.

Justus says, "Is that a song of worship?"

"It is, but whoever is singing cannot carry a tune in a bucket," Eleazer responds.

I think I recognize the voice. I hurry to the door, pressing my ear firmly against the rough wood.

Could it really be Paul?

The voice grows closer and is unmistakable—it is indeed Paul, my fellow apostle and dear friend!

I call out, "Paul, it is Peter! Be strong in the Lord, brother!"

The singing abruptly stops; Paul calls out, "Peter, my—."

He is suddenly interrupted, and the only sound I hear is that of Paul being kicked and beaten. I pray fervently for my brother in the Lord. Turning to my fellow prisoners, I stop long enough to whisper, "Would you please pray?"

"We already are," Josiah answers.

Once more, risking the fury of the guards, I shout, "The Lord is with you, Paul!"

Within minutes, a key is put in the lock of my door; I quickly scramble to get out of the way. The door opens, and a furious guard delivers a sharp blow across my face. He shouts, "Maybe that will help you keep your mouth shut, you stupid Christian!"

Cursing, he storms out, slamming the door behind him.

Warm liquid gushes from my mouth. Wiping the blood on my ragged sleeve, I spit out several pieces of teeth.

"That was foolish," Eleazer states.

"It was worth it; they stopped beating Paul, didn't they?" I answer.

Eleazer grunts in response.

"Who is Paul?" Laban asks.

"Paul is one of my dearest friends and also a fellow Jewish brother. He, too, is an apostle of Jesus Christ. Before he came to know Jesus as the Messiah, he was called Saul and was a highly respected member of the Jews. He was adamantly opposed to Jesus. As a matter of fact, he was so convinced that Jesus was a fraud that he went about the cities arresting anyone who followed Him. It was during a trip to Damascus to persecute the Christians there that Jesus appeared to him in a vision. After that encounter, Paul was blind for several days. Then the Lord sent one of His servants to restore his sight. Since that time, which was just over thirty years ago, Paul has been a faithful follower of the Lord, enduring much hardship and persecution for his faith."[54]

"That is quite a testimony," Justus says.

"There are many just like Paul out there, my friends. The Christian walk, as you are realizing, is not one of ease and comfort, but rather it is one of sacrifice, love, suffering and denying of self," I answer.

"What's the point then? Why become a follower of Jesus if the result is suffering? I can find enough trouble on my own without adding to it," Eleazer states.

"You asked what the point is; I will tell you. The point is that you, my friend, are destined to spend eternity in hell where the fire is never quenched and where worms will feast on you. The point is that you are a sinner in need of a Savior, and there is only one Savior, and His name is Jesus. The point is that without Jesus you are doomed; you have no hope; you will never know peace, not now, not ever. You see, Eleazer, you need Him more than you need air or food or water.

"It is true; there is a price to be paid, but it is nothing compared to what you gain. Everyone wastes his life on something; why not waste it on Jesus? Why not suffer for the sake of the gospel rather than suffering according to your evil desires and selfish ambitions?

"The Christian life is so much more than suffering, my friend. It is a life filled with great joy and tremendous rewards," I answer.

Wiping the blood from my mouth and chin, I wait hoping that Eleazer will finally surrender.

Before he can respond, the sound of fast approaching guards fill the hall. I quickly back away from the door and embrace the post in hopes that they won't notice that I am not chained.

The door swings open and my dear friend, Malchus, walks in followed closely by Brutus. Thankfully, they left their torch in the holder just outside the door.

"So, you know Paul?" Brutus asks.

"I do, he is a Jewish brother and a friend."

"Then you will be happy to know that he is going to suffer the same fate as you. He is going to die! But, before he dies, he will get to know me really well," Brutus says as he rubs his hands together in sick anticipation.

"Paul will pay whatever price necessary," I answer.

"We'll see about that," he replies and then turns his attention to my fellow prisoners saying, "You would be wise to avoid listening to this old man's words, for he is foolish and believes old women's tales!"

Scrambling to get the attention back on me and off of them, I say, "Brutus, I speak only the truth and you know it is true. You just aren't willing to—."

"Shut up!" he says as he delivers several blows to my rib cage.

Malchus takes a step forward. I can see the compassion in his eyes. I quickly speak, "Brutus, there is One who cares about you—."

"I said, 'Shut up!' "

"How can I when—."

"What don't you understand about those two words?" He says as he pulls me to my feet by the hair of my head.

"You stink!" he says slamming me face first into the stone wall.

An explosion of stars fills my head. From some far away place, I hear Malchus saying something about mercy. My world suddenly grows dark and quiet, too quiet.

Sometime later I wake to find that I am once more chained hand and foot to a post. My head is pounding. The right side of my face is swollen so much that I cannot open my eye. My mouth is crusted shut with dried blood. With great effort, I manage to scrape the thick crust off so that I can speak.

"What happened to Malchus?" I ask just as soon as I am able.

"It is you that we are worried about. Are you okay?

What damage has Brutus done this time?" Josiah asks.

"Not anything that won't heal, but what of Malchus? He didn't intervene, did he?"

"When you fell, Brutus began kicking you. Malchus shouted, 'In the name of Jesus, stop!' To my surprise, Brutus did exactly that. But, after a few minutes, he turned toward Malchus. Even in the dim light, it was clear to see that he was filled with rage. Then, as if seeing a ghost, he suddenly turned white and began to shake violently. I looked to see what frightened him, but saw absolutely nothing. Malchus then said, 'Brutus, not only I, but also my entire household has become a follower of Jesus. And you would be wise to do the same, my friend.'

"It was then that Brutus dropped to his knees like a stone dropped in a well. It appeared that he fainted. I was afraid that it was a trick. Malchus wasted no time. He quickly knelt beside your unconscious body and prayed as he wiped the gushing blood from your nose and mouth.

"It was just as if God Himself was keeping Brutus unconscious because once Malchus got the bleeding to stop, Brutus woke up. He suddenly jumped to his feet and called for a guard to chain you hand and feet to the post.

"Brutus then grabbed Malchus by the hair and drug him out, cursing as he went. We have heard nothing since then," Laban answers.

"Peter, tell us, are you badly hurt?" Josiah asks.

"Not badly, my friend. I have a splitting headache and feel very weak, but that is all."

Eleazer mockingly says, "Well now, we finally hear the truth. That is probably the truest words you have spoken. You are indeed weak, Peter."

"What are you saying?" Justus exclaims, "Peter is the strongest man I have ever known, besides Jesus, that is!"

"He is weak because he won't do what is necessary to free himself from this cesspool and from these heartless guards. We are criminals; we deserve to die, but Peter has committed no crime. He can free himself with a simple confession, but he is too weak to save himself. He is too weak to fight. If he were strong, he would deny Jesus and live!" Eleazer exclaims, his voice shaking.

"Eleazer, you are right; I am weak. Before I came to know Jesus, I thought I was strong and thought that I could do anything. And then, after becoming one of His followers, I soon became extremely prideful; I felt powerful, invincible. But, the day came when I learned just how weak I really was and just how needy I was. In that hour, I came face to face with my cowardice and realized that I needed Someone stronger than myself to be in charge of my life. I needed a Savior.

"Up to that point, I had been my own hero, but a day came when I denied the Lord not just once but three times. At that point, I discovered that there is only one hero in this life, and His name is Jesus. It was then that I determined, by the grace of God, that I would never again rely on my own strength. I made a decision to make Jesus the center of my existence and not myself. I also decided that I would never again deny my King, no matter what.

"So, I must agree with you, my friend. I am weak and will remain weak all the days of my life, for when I am weak it is then that I am strong because I lean on the One who promised to never leave me nor forsake me."[55]

Eleazer is silent. I pray for his salvation.

Justus says, "I have a lot to learn in a very short amount of time, Peter."

"We all do," Laban adds.

I respond, "I do not know whether I have weeks, days or hours left, but I know that the laying aside of my earthly body is at hand, our Lord Jesus Christ has made that very clear to me.[56]

"When I am taken from you, remember that your prayers

accomplish much. For example, look at the prophet Elijah; he was a man with a nature like ours, and he prayed earnestly that it would not rain. For three years and six months, it did not rain on the earth. Then he prayed again, and the sky poured rain, and the earth produced its fruit. You are no different from Elijah, my friends. Just as Elijah prayed and saw the things on this earth change, so can you."[57]

"I haven't seen much change around here as a result of your prayers," Eleazer states.

Before I have a chance to respond, Laban explodes, "What! Are you blind, or did you leave your brain outside the prison gates? We asked Jesus to heal you, and He did it! I would say that God certainly changed your circumstances as a result of prayer! He has healed Peter several times. And, just look at me and Josiah and Justus—in a short time, Jesus has captured our attention and is in the process of securing our affections. Are you just plain stupid or just too proud to admit that you are in need? You are an arrogant, foolish—."

I interrupt, "Laban, if you want sheep to follow the Shepherd, you must never beat them, but lovingly feed them the fruit of the Spirit, which is love, joy, peace, patience, kindness, goodness, faithfulness, gentleness and self-control."[58]

"It's just that I am tired of his mouth, and I am tired of his attitude," he replies.

Eleazer jumps in and says, "I don't need you to defend me, Peter. And I certainly don't appreciate the fact that you would compare me to a sheep, which is one of the dumbest animals in existence. For your information, I am a highly educated man, and I don't need anyone to lead me anywhere."

"We all are like sheep, Eleazer, and we all need a Shepherd. Therefore, I would encourage each one of you to draw close to the Son of God that you might be transformed into His image."

"Peter, I apologize to you and also to Eleazer. Please forgive me for my rude comments," Laban says.

"I forgive you," I respond.

Eleazer mumbles something about what Laban can do with his apology.

Ignoring him, I continue, "My friends, let us not lose heart in doing good for in due time we shall reap if we do not grow weary," I say.[59]

"I believe you, Peter, but I must admit that I still have my moments when I wonder if what you have told us is really true," Laban confesses.

"Now that's the first sensible thought you have had," Eleazer says sounding slightly happy.

Ignoring him I respond, "Laban, it is good for you to search for the truth because those who search for it finds it."[60]

Josiah adds, "Though we have not seen Jesus, we love Him, and though we cannot see Him now, we still believe in Him."[61]

"I won't believe in something that I cannot see," Eleazer says.

"Do you believe in the air you breathe, which is impossible to see? And what about Abraham? You can't see him, but I know that you believe that he was a real person who really lived. And what about love? You can't see that, but surely you believe in love," I ask.

"Ask me about hate, Peter. I can't see that, but I certainly believe that it is real." Eleazer states.

"Eleazer, what makes you so mean?" Laban asks.

"If I wasn't stuck in here with you, I would be a much happier man," he answers.

"My friends, you do not have enough time to argue," I say trying to diffuse an unproductive situation. "For the sake of peace, let us turn our attention back to the King and the time He walked among weak human beings like ourselves."

CHAPTER TEN

The following morning, Jesus called us twelve apostles to His side and said, "I am giving you authority to drive out unclean spirits and to heal every disease and weakness."

What!? Are we to work His works? Are we to perform miracles and set the demonized free? Are we to wield His sword of authority and power?

I surveyed our little group, a group made up of my brother, Andrew, and also James, John, Phillip, Bartholomew, Thomas, Matthew, James the son of Alphaeus, Thaddaeus, Simon the Zealot and Judas Iscariot.

What a weak, pitiful group we are! We are nothing more than common laborers and quite young. It certainly isn't our talents or our past achievements that cause the Master to bestow such awesome power on us. Actually, I can think of no reason for Jesus to grant us authority to do such deeds. About the only thing we have in our favor is our love and devotion for Him, which is still so immature and self-seeking.

One of the things that amazes me most about Jesus is how deeply He loves and cares for us even when we mess up. He loves weak people, and He loves those who are devoted to Him. His affections are not based on one's wealth, education, social position or refinement. Those things do not move His heart, but a heart that voluntarily loves Him never fails to capture His attention.

I have learned so much from the Master. I have witnessed numerous miracles, heard great teachings, learned how to pray and how to live. I love being one of His followers, one of His apostles!

Jesus continued, "I am sending you out with power to heal, but do not go into the territory of the Gentiles and do not enter any town in Samaria, but go rather to the lost sheep of the house of Israel."

"If we go, what message are we to bring?" Thomas asked.

"Say this, 'The Kingdom of heaven is near.' Heal the sick, raise the dead, cleanse the lepers, cast out demons. Freely you have received, now freely give.

"Go in pairs; go at once. Do not return to your homes, but go as you are. Do not take money in your belts—no gold, no silver, no copper. Do not take a pack, an extra shirt, shoes or a walking stick—a worker should be given what he needs.[62]

"If you have any of these items already with you, that is fine, but if not, go anyway; you can do without them!

"When you come to a town or village, look for someone trustworthy and stay with him until you leave. When you enter his house, bless it saying, 'Peace be to this house!'

"If the people of that house or town do not welcome you or listen to you, leave that place and shake its dust from your feet!"

It would be the height of insult for us to shake off the dust of our feet in a Jewish town not to mention in a Jewish home! He is asking us to do to the Jews what we do to the Gentiles every time we pass through their cities! Surely, He cannot mean it!

"I tell you, it will be more tolerable on the day of judgment for the people of Sodom and Gomorrah than it will be for the city that rejects you.

"Pay attention! I am sending you out like sheep among wolves; therefore, be as wise and prudent as snakes and as harmless as doves. Be on guard, for there will be people who will hand you over to the Sanhedrin, and you will be flogged in their synagogues.

"Because of Me, you will be brought before governors and kings as a testimony to them and also to the Gentiles. But when they bring you to trial, do not worry about what to say or how to say it. When that time comes, you will be given what you are to say; it will be the Spirit of your heavenly Father speaking through you."

I don't think I like what He is saying very much.

"A brother will betray his brother to death and a father his child; children will turn against their parents and have them put to death. Everyone will hate you because of Me, but whoever holds out to the end will be preserved from harm."

Now, I know that I don't like what He is saying. How can people hate us when we are going to be healing their sick and delivering them from demons?

"When you are persecuted in one town, leave there and go to another. Yes indeed, I tell you, you will not finish going through the towns of Israel before the Son of Man comes."

I am greatly confused. Are we to travel throughout all of Israel, and then the Messiah will come?

"A disciple is not above his teacher is he? A slave is not greater than his master is he? It is enough for a disciple that he become like his teacher and a slave like his master. Now if people have called the head of the house Beelzebub, how much more will they malign the members of his household!

"So do not fear them; for there is nothing covered that will not be uncovered, or hidden that will not be known. What I tell you in the dark, speak in the light; what is whispered in your ear, proclaim from the housetops.

"Do not fear those who kill the body but are powerless to kill the soul. Rather, fear him who can destroy both soul and body in hell. Dangers are indeed coming, but fear not.

"Sparrows are sold for next to nothing, two for a penny, yet not one of them will fall to the ground without your Father's consent. As for you, every hair on your head has been counted. So, do not be afraid. If God cares for something as insignificant as sparrows, how much more does He care for His people? You are worth more than many sparrows.

"Whoever acknowledges Me in the presence of others, I will also acknowledge in the presence of My Father in heaven.

"Do not suppose that I have come to bring peace to the land. I did not come to bring peace, but a sword! For I have come to set a man against his father, a daughter against her mother, a daughter-in-law against her mother-in-law, so that a man's enemies will be the members of his own household."

He must be talking about using the sword against Rome.

"Whoever loves his father or mother more than he loves Me is not worthy of Me. Anyone who loves his son or daughter more than he loves Me is not worthy of Me. And anyone who does not take up his cross and follow Me is not worthy of Me. Whoever finds his own life will lose it, but the person who loses his life for My sake will find it.

"Whoever receives you receives Me, and whoever receives Me receives the One who sent Me. Anyone who receives a prophet because he is a prophet will receive the reward of a prophet. Anyone who receives a righteous man because he is righteous will receive the reward of a righteous man. Indeed, if someone gives a cup of cold water to one of these little ones because he is My disciple—yes!— I tell you, he will certainly not lose his reward!"

At the time, I understood very little of what Jesus said. I knew only that we were to go and heal the sick, cast out demons, and tell everyone that the kingdom of God was at hand.

After completing our instructions, Jesus sent us out in pairs and He departed from there to teach and preach in the surrounding cities.[63]

CHAPTER ELEVEN

I stop talking because my head is throbbing and my mouth hurts. "Oh, Lord give me strength and heal my body once again," I quietly pray.

Josiah asks, "Peter, do you need to rest?"

"Perhaps just a moment, my friends."

Carefully leaning my aching head against the post, I fall into a fitful sleep. When I wake, I hear snoring.

They must have needed to sleep as well.

I sit in silence, focusing on my King. I long to be with Him where He is. I am so focused that I fail to hear the approaching footsteps. Our prison door groans opens, and a container is dropped by the door. "Enjoy your meal, boys," says an unfamiliar voice.

The door slams shut.

Eleazer curses under his breath.

"Peter, are you awake?" Laban asks.

"I am."

"Are you feeling better?" he asks.

"Yes."

"Peter, I've been thinking about how the twelve of you

were sent out to heal the sick and cast out demons. It's one thing for Jesus to heal people, but to think that He asked you to do the things that He did is amazing! Oh, I would have loved to see that!" Justus exclaims.

"At the time, I was very excited. It is almost intoxicating to be able to affect such changes in people, my friends.

"What Jesus asked us to do was a challenge and an adventure. I was ready to take on the world! It was with great zeal and unbridled energy that I went with John into the surrounding cities. It was a good thing that Jesus told us precisely where to go and what to say because I was so zealous that there is no telling what I would have preached. None of us, especially myself, knew what we were doing, and we were so spiritually immature that we could have done a lot of damage had Jesus not given us such clear instructions."

"Tell us, what was it like to have power to cast out demons?" Josiah asks.

"I'd be lying if I said it wasn't exciting, but I later learned that seeing a soul enter the Kingdom of heaven is even more rewarding than seeing a temporal body healed. Do not pursue power, my friends, for there is much danger in that. Just as there is danger in pursuing religion without relationship. Jesus is and always will be what you should pursue. The authority and power to heal the sick and cast out demons are all part of living in the Kingdom, but they are not the prize. The prize is a Man, a King who loves His people."

"Because of your power, I suppose you became quite famous and popular," Eleazer sarcastically says.

"On the contrary, my brother, the people understood that the healing power came from Jesus. They knew that the only reason we were able to heal was because we had been with Him and He had commissioned us to do so. He was the One who became more popular as was evident by the fact that the people of Galilee did not wonder who we were, but they wondered only who Jesus was."

"And, pray tell me, just what was your message to these poor country folk?" Eleazer asks.

Ignoring his tone, I answer, "Jesus knew all too well that we were not ready to be trusted with anything more than the little revelation we had. We were told to proclaim that the Kingdom of heaven was at hand and to bid men to repent that they might be ready for its coming. As for our understanding of the message, we were like young children still in school. The only thing we really understood was that repentance was necessary for citizenship into this Kingdom.[64]

"As for those we delivered the message to, most viewed the Kingdom as the restoration of Israel's political independence and economic prosperity like unto the days of old. That was what I thought as well. Our message was as foreign to the people as water is to the desert.

"What the people really wanted and looked for was a kingdom on earth where they could live in peace. They wanted a just, Jewish government, and most importantly, they wanted to have plenty to eat and drink."

Eleazer responds, "I can certainly understand why my Jewish brothers would have trouble with your message, Peter. Every Jewish man knows that the Kingdom is yet to come. After all, we are still under Roman rule, in case you haven't noticed."

"The Kingdom has already come and is yet to come," I answer.[65]

"That remains to be seen," Eleazer responds.

"And I pray that the veil will be removed from your eyes that you might see before it is too late," I answer.

Justus asks, "Why did Jesus forbid you to go into our Gentile cities?"

"And what about my people, the Samaritans? Why did

He forbid you to go there?" Josiah adds.

"Jesus knew all too well that we were, at that time in our lives, not fit to go among the Gentiles and Samaritans. Our hearts were too small, our thinking too narrow, our prejudices too strong. We were still too Jewish in our thinking and nothing like our King. I am certain that it was for their sake that He did not send us to the Gentiles and Samaritans, not that we desired to go to them. We had much to learn before He could trust us to go to them."

"Peter, since you have received this miracle-working power, then command our prison door to open. Better yet, command Nero to set us free," Eleazer bitterly says.

"Eleazer, you do not know what you are saying. What I will do is tell you about the One who can set you free in the areas that really matter."

CHAPTER TWELVE

The twelve of us went from village to village anointing the sick with oil, and to our amazement, the people were healed right before our eyes. We cast out demons and proclaimed that the Kingdom of heaven was at hand. I felt like a little child who had been given his first puppy and enjoyed it immensely but was not exactly sure what to do with it.

Several weeks passed. It was early spring, shortly before Passover. John and I were speaking to some shepherds about the Kingdom when a young man ran past us saying, "Have you heard? Herod has beheaded John the baptizer!"

Oh, someone tell me that it is not true!

Without saying farewell to the shepherds, John and I hurried after the young man, seeking more information. My heart sank as I heard the gruesome details. It seemed that Herod had a party. The daughter of his unlawful wife, Herodias, danced for him and pleased him greatly. In fact, it pleased him so much that he made an oath to give her anything she wanted, up to half of his kingdom. Herodias hated John because he had boldly proclaimed that it was sinful for Herod to be married to her because she was his brother's wife. Being prompted by her mother, the girl asked for John's head on a platter.

It was true—our friend and teacher had been beheaded by king Herod![66]

Without taking food or rest, John and I hurried to the next town in search of Jesus. Along the way, we met Phillip and Matthew who had also heard the news. When we entered the city, we were told that John's disciples had already claimed his body and given him a proper burial. They had also delivered the news to Jesus who was last seen in Capernaum. We wasted no time setting out for Capernaum. After several days of searching, we found Him in one of the surrounding villages.

Unfortunately, the crowds from Capernaum followed us. His seclusion was short-lived as the people flocked to Jesus like starving sheep in search of green pasture. They brought their sick and beseeched Him to heal them, which He gladly did. Throughout the day, the people were so many, coming and going, that we could not find a single moment to talk with Him, neither was there any time for us to eat.

Before nightfall, the other apostles arrived, having heard the painful news. We tried to get away from the crowds, but they continued to follow Jesus. We were tired, hungry and emotionally hurting. My patience was growing thin.

Turning to James and John, I said, "Can't they see that we'd like some time with Jesus? After all, we've been gone for weeks."

John replied, "Can't they see the pain in His eyes, the deep sorrow etched on His face, the fatigue?"

I followed John's gaze and clearly saw what he alone had seen. "He does appear to be weary," I responded.

Shortly thereafter, to my great delight, Jesus withdrew

from the crowd and joined us saying, "Come, follow Me."

"Where to Master? The crowds will follow us wherever we go," I responded.

"To an isolated place where you can eat and take some rest," He answered.

We followed Jesus to the sea where a boat was quickly hired. We climbed in, and Jesus instructed us to sail for Bethsaida.

Bethsaida is outside the dominion of Herod, on the northeastern extremity of the lake, but near Capernaum. It is a small fishing village and would certainly offer us some much needed rest and privacy.

Bethsaida is close enough to Capernaum to walk to, so why the boat?

One look behind me at the crowded shore answered my question. The people were in emotional chaos because of the murder of John the baptizer. It would not take much for them to attempt an uprising.

It was a windless day, so it took longer than normal to travel the four miles across the lake and the ten miles round the top to Bethsaida. I was thankful for the delay because it gave us several hours to report to each other and to Jesus the extraordinary things that had happened on our journeys.

I was the first to speak, "John and I went among the villages preaching the good news and healing all who were sick, casting out demons and restoring the lepers. It was exhilarating to see such power at work. Our exploits were so great that even Herod heard about the works that we did. Just this morning we heard that he was saying that John the Baptist had risen from the dead. While some of the people said that Elijah had appeared, others said that one of the prophets of old had risen again."

Jesus said nothing. As the others gave their reports, I looked closely at my Teacher. John was right; He did look weary, and there was a deep sadness in His eyes.

Of course, how could I have been so blind, so selfish—His cousin was just murdered. Of course He is sad.

Jesus graciously listened as the others told of blind eyes seeing, lame men walking and the demonized being set free.

As Bethsaida came into sight, my heart sank—the beach was completely filled with people who were waving and shouting at us.

There must be several thousand people waiting for Jesus! Where did they come from, and how did they know?

My question was quickly answered by a young man who shouted, "Master! We saw You leave so we ran around the top of the lake and have been waiting for You!"

Surveying the crowd, Jesus sighed deeply. I thought that He was disappointed because of the crowds, but not so, for He said, "Simon, look at them! They are like sheep who have no shepherd."

What?!

"Simon, they have no one to lead them, to protect or feed them. They are in great need, my friend."

Why isn't He annoyed? I certainly am. These people knew that the Master was leaving so that He could get away from the crowds and find some much needed rest. After all, His cousin was just murdered, He hasn't eaten all day or taken any rest, and still they come making demands on Him!

I was ready to protest when Jesus laid His hand on my arm and said, "Simon, they need a Shepherd, they need someone to care for them."

I looked into His eyes and saw life and hope and love. I saw compassion deeper than the deepest well. How could I argue with that? I merely nodded.

Our ship was eagerly met by several young men who dragged it to shore. With a smile, Jesus leaped over the side of the boat and immediately began teaching the people and healing all who were sick.[67]

CHAPTER THIRTEEN

Hearing a guard, I stop. The door opens, and Malchus walks in with a dimly lit lamp. He quietly closes the door behind him. I am so very glad to see him!

"Malchus, my brother, tell me what has happened since your encounter with Brutus?" I whisper.

Malchus kneels beside me, giving me a long cool drink as he answers, "Brutus beat me thoroughly but surprisingly, did nothing further. It appears that he has told no one of my confession. If he had, I would not be here today but would either be in chains or with the Lord in Paradise.

"It is quite strange, but I have not seen him or heard anything about him since that day. I must say that his lack of retaliation towards me is a mystery that I am extremely grateful for, Peter."

"This is indeed good news and an answer to my prayers, Malchus!"

"It certainly is. I have come to not only bring you food and water, but also to relay a message to you from Paul."

"Pray, tell me what it is!" I respond most eagerly.

"Paul said, 'Tell Peter that we are afflicted in every way, but we are not crushed. We are perplexed, but we are not in despair. We are persecuted, but we are not forsaken; struck down, but we are not destroyed.'[68]

"Those were his exact words, for he had me memorize them," Malchus says as he carefully places a piece of bread in my still very painful mouth.

"They are words of life, my friend, and words that we must never forget. How is Paul? Is he badly beaten?" I ask.

"He is recovering nicely. His gaze is set like flint on one thing, and that is serving Jesus and those he comes in contact with. The church in my home is praying for him as well as for all of you; they send their greetings. You will be glad to hear that souls are being saved in great numbers. It seems the more Nero persecutes us, the more people turn to Jesus."

I respond, "It is forever true. And blessed is the one who perseveres under trial; for once he has been approved, he will receive the crown of life which the Lord has promised to those who love Him."[69]

Malchus adds, "You and Paul and many others in this fortress all have a crown of life waiting for you."

"As do you, my friend," I say.

"Peter, your lips are very swollen and most likely infected, but I expected that and have brought an ointment which will help. But first, you must eat more, and then I will apply it."

"Your kindness is recorded in heaven, Malchus."

"My actions are not heroic, for I do only what Jesus or any other Christian would do if they were here," he answers.

Standing, Malchus quietly says, "I am a bearer of good gifts today, for I have not only brought bread, but also raisins."

Raisins! I cannot remember the last time I had raisins!

He quickly feeds us, praying for each of us, even Eleazer.

He then gives us as much water as we can drink.

"I must go before I am found out," he whispers as he spreads the last of the ointment on my mouth.

"Malchus, would you thank my brother Paul for his encouragement and give him a message for me?"

"I would be glad to do so."

"Tell him not to lose heart even though our outer man is decaying, yet our inner man is being renewed day by day. Momentary, light affliction is producing in us an eternal weight of glory far beyond all comparison. Encourage him to look not at the things which are seen, but at the things which are not seen; for the things which are seen are temporal, but the things which are not seen are eternal."

"I will tell him as soon the Lord makes the way," Malchus answers.

"And, Malchus, thank you again. You are a messenger of the Lord making it possible for us to stay alive in conditions that are designed to take our lives. My prayer is that I would live long enough to see everyone in this cell come to a saving knowledge of Christ Jesus. And you, my friend and brother, are helping to make that possible."

"And I will not cease praying for that very thing," Malchus responds laying his hand on my shoulder.

"Malchus, one last thing. I have a message for the church that meets in your home. Encourage them to be careful that ministry does not become their god. The Lord jealously desires us for Himself. He will not share us with other loves, even if it is something that is good and right and ought to be done.

"If we put anything before our relationship with Jesus, even our work for Him, we will eventually become ensnared by it, and our love for the Master will soon grow cold. Therefore, encourage them to gird their minds for action, keep sober in spirit and fix their hope completely on the grace to be brought to them at the revelation of Jesus Christ.[70]

"In so doing, they will obtain the salvation of their souls as the outcome of their faith.[71] Remind them to fervently love one another from the heart, brother.[72] And may grace and peace be yours in the fullest measure."

"And may the Lord be with you all," Malchus responds.

As the sound of Malchus's footsteps fades into the distance, Laban speaks, "Eleazer, you may not believe what Peter has told us about the Master, but are you not moved by Malchus's willingness to risk his life for our benefit?"

Eleazer responds, "Peter, just continue with your story so that I can get some sleep without anyone bothering me."

"Eleazer, I will continue that you might hear and live, for I have not given up on you and neither has the King of kings," I respond.

CHAPTER FOURTEEN

After ministering to the crowds, Jesus turned and said, "Come, let us go to the hillside!"

He led the charge up the grassy hill. To my disappointment, the great multitude followed. When we arrived at its pinnacle, Jesus called to the people to gather around. I chose a place as close to Jesus as I could get and reclined on the thick, spring grass.

As much as I disliked the demanding crowds, I had to admit that it was a beautiful sight. The masses stretched across the great expanse of green grass in their brightly colored garments. They looked like a garden in full bloom with the face of every flower turned upward, toward Jesus.

Those who were lame, crippled, blind and dumb were laid at Jesus' feet. He spent the entire afternoon healing the sick and teaching them many things.

As the sun slid beneath the horizon, the last sick person was healed.

I don't know how Jesus does it; I am emotionally and physically exhausted, and all I did was watch.

Hurrying to His side, I said, "Jesus, this is a remote

place, and it is late. Send the people away, so that they can buy food and find lodging in the farms and towns nearby."

He looked across the vast multitude spread out like a large flock of sheep. He then turned to Phillip and asked, "Tell Me, where can we buy bread so that these people can eat?"

Shaking his head, Phillip answered, "Half a year's wages wouldn't buy enough bread for a crowd this size, and if it were, there would only be enough for each to have a bite! I suggest that You send them away, Jesus."

Phillip is right. And besides that, there is no place we could buy enough bread for this many people. The feast of Passover is coming up; the people have already begun reducing their bread supplies in anticipation of the feast. We would be hard pressed to find even half the amount of bread needed.

Placing His hand on Phillip's shoulder Jesus responded, "The people don't need to go away! You give them something to eat!"

I looked at Andrew, James and John who looked at me. I whispered, "There are thousands here. How is it that we could feed a multitude such as this?"

John shrugged, and James shook his head.

Jesus continued, "How many loaves do you have?"

Phillip looked around and answered, "I don't know."

"Go and find out," Jesus said.

After inquiring, we discovered that none of us had brought food. "Surely someone has something," I said feeling quite disturbed.

We inquired among the people but discovered that the news was grim. With sinking hearts, we returned to Jesus. Andrew reported, "A young lad has five barley rolls and two very small salt fish, but what are these for so many people?"

Jesus gave no answer. Andrew continued, "Master, this will feed only one or two at the most."

Barley rolls were the cheapest and coarsest of all bread; it was the food of the poorest of the poor. And the two tiny fish were the kind we used as relish for bread. This small amount was barely worth mentioning.

Jesus answered, "Instruct the people to sit on the grass in groups of fifty and one hundred."

Without any understanding, we obeyed. The hillside was completely covered with people. I quickly counted the groups. My stomach sank as I calculated there to be about five thousand men, not counting the women and children!

What does He have in mind?

Jesus took the barley and the fish and lifted them up to heaven, saying, "Blessed art Thou, Jehovah our God, King of the world, Who causes bread to come forth from the earth."

He then broke a roll in two pieces, and handed it to Andrew who then passed it on. Jesus continued to break the bread, and we distributed it to the people until everyone had eaten and had their fill.

As we reclined beside Jesus on the fragrant green grass, He instructed us to gather the leftover pieces, so that nothing got wasted.

From the five barley loaves and two fish, we filled all twelve of our coarse wicker baskets with the leftover pieces! The multitude watched closely. A whisper spread throughout the ranks, "This must be the Prophet who is supposed to come into the world! This Prophet must be Israel's long expected Messiah—our King!"

Jesus was the hero of the hour. More than anything, the people wanted freedom from Roman rule, peace and prosperity. I knew what they were thinking because the same thoughts were running through my mind. They saw in this Miracle Worker the One who would conquer Rome and usher in peace for Israel. Whispers of making Him king quickly circulated throughout the crowd.

The people are ready to make Him king. And why not? After all, imagine what could be accomplished for Israel if Jesus ruled us instead of Rome. Never have I seen such a dramatic display of authority and miraculous power. With Jesus as King, no one in Israel would ever suffer from hunger or disease.

Turning to Jesus, our eyes met. There was still the fatigue and pain, but even greater than that was the extreme kindness that I saw there.

He stood motioning for the twelve of us to follow. Eager to do so, we grabbed a basket and hurried after Him. As He led us down the hillside to the sea, we distributed the leftovers.

Standing beside the boat, Jesus said to us, "Go ahead of Me to Bethsaida while I send the multitudes away."

I hesitated, but Jesus placed His hand on my shoulder and said, "Peter, the people intend to take Me by force to make Me their king."

What's so bad about that?

"Not now, not this way," He responded to my unspoken thought.

He must be trying to protect us from the zeal of the crowd, for Galilee is a revolution just waiting to happen because of John's murder and Jesus' demonstration of power. These two things could easily cause a revolt.

I looked over Jesus' shoulder and saw the multitude rushing towards Him. With a nod, I climbed into the boat. As Andrew shoved the boat out, Jesus turned and addressed the crowds.

Later, from a short distance away, I watched as the crowds dispersed and one solitary Man ascended the mountain.[73]

CHAPTER FIFTEEN

Eleazer asks, "Peter, surely you do not believe those wild tales, do you?"

"I am so convinced that Jesus is the Son of God, the promised Messiah, that I will die for Him," I answer.

"Others have died for causes less glorious than the one you lay claim to," Eleazer responds.

"Yes, that is true, but I want to ask you the same question I asked Brutus, have you ever known of one who would die for a lie? If, as you insinuate, I am lying, then why would I not recant and save my life? Why would I die for something that I knew was a lie? Not even a fool would do so. And, Eleazer, I am not the first of the apostles to die. John and myself are the only ones left alive of the original twelve apostles. The others, with the exception of Judas, died a martyr's death for the sake of Jesus Christ."

Eleazer does not respond. The sound of dripping water from some far off place echoes through the hallway. My lips are cracked and bleeding, my head screams for relief, and my body is racked with pain from being chained to this post.

I continue, "Eleazer, I would not have endured the horrible tortures that were inflicted upon me for the past nine months had I not been certain beyond any shadow of a doubt that Jesus is indeed the Son of God. I know that He is who He claimed to be. I personally witnessed Him do things that only God could do. And besides all the miracles, the extravagant compassion, the teachings that reached beyond this world to another, besides all that, I saw the resurrected Jesus after He had been dead for three days.

"Eleazer, Jesus is alive! He is fully God and fully Man sitting on a throne, and the day is coming when He will return to Jerusalem and establish His Kingdom in its fullness. Heaven is coming to earth, my friend, and we will see a righteous King ruling over all the earth. Those who have entered into a covenant with the King will be residents of His Kingdom. We will be a worshipping bride, an eternal partner who will love Him so much that fear does not rule us.[74]

"God is sovereign, but there is an element of partnership between the King and His Bride. Mark my word, there is a day coming when we will rule and reign with Him, but that will not happen until the leaders of Israel say, 'Blessed is He who comes in the name of the Lord.'"[75]

"That will never happen," Eleazer responds.

"It will most certainly happen because Jesus said that it would happen! This King, who existed in the form of God, did not regard equality with God a thing to be grasped but emptied Himself and became a bond-servant. And being found in the appearance of a Man, He humbled himself by becoming obedient to the point of death, even death on a cross. Therefore, God highly exalted Him and bestowed on Him the name which is above every name, that at the name of Jesus every knee should bow, all who are in heaven and on earth, and under the earth and every tongue will confess that Jesus is Lord. Believe me, Eleazer, there is a day coming when every tongue will confess that Jesus Christ is Lord, to the glory of God the Father, and that includes you and our Jewish brothers.[76]

"Eleazer, Jesus was and will forevermore be the King of not only the Jews, but also of all who accept His invitation to become a resident of His Kingdom. As for me, I will gladly die for Him just as He gladly died for me!"

Eleazer is silent; I wait and pray. The dripping water seems to grow louder causing me to realize just how thirsty I am.

"Eleazer, imagine if you would, king Solomon laying aside his power, wealth, kingdom, title, honor and position so that he could become a commoner and live among his subjects. Now imagine that he did that because of his great love for his subjects! And then add to the equation that king Solomon knew before he laid aside his glory that the very ones he was trying to help would kill him. And still he did it anyway.

"Well, my brother, that is what Jesus did, only more so because He laid aside perfection and glory and beauty and greatness to dress Himself in a garment of dirt by becoming a Man. And He knew that it would cost Him everything, but His love for us was so great that it outweighed the price He would pay. He did what He did for love, my friend."

Eleazer remarks, "Just how did He die?"

"The Lord died on a cross, but before that He was cruelly beaten. He suffered great atrocities at the hands of men, and yet He uttered no defense or threats in return. He simply entrusted Himself to His Father, the One who judges righteously.

"This same Jesus bore our sins in His body on a cross that we might die to sin and live to righteousness. He became a criminal so that you could be proclaimed innocent. He took the punishment you and I certainly deserve. By His wounds you were healed."

"By his wounds, I was healed? What does that mean?" Josiah asks.

"Jesus died for your sins once for all. He exchanged His life for yours, the just for the unjust that He might bring us to His Father and heal our diseases both physically and spiritually.

"He was put to death in the flesh, but He was made alive in the Spirit. And, it is for this reason that I will endure whatever tortures may come my way."

There is a long silence. I pray silently that the Holy Spirit would capture Eleazer's heart.

Eleazer finally responds, "I am angry, but I am tired of being angry. I am tired through and through. I am tired of fighting, and I am tired of living.

"Peter, you made an interesting point when you pointed out the reality of how insane it would be for you to allow yourself to suffer for a lie. Which leads me to the only intelligent conclusion there is, and that is that you certainly believe that what you are saying is true. You believe that Jesus died and came to life again. You believe that he was the Son of God and in him is eternal life. You believe that he is a God of love, mercy and compassion. I understand that, but what I don't understand is why you won't deny Jesus long enough to get out of this place. Why is that?"

"Because I am in love with a King who loved me more than life itself. Because I know the Truth, and the Truth is a King, not a law written on stones. Because I cannot live without Him. Because I cannot stand without His mercy, goodness and love! Because I cannot lie! Because Jesus said that He would deny everyone who denied Him."[77]

"You will surely die then," Eleazer says obviously shaken.

"I will surely die, but I will surely live again. For a believer, death is but a stepping stone to the real life, to a place of perfection that is filled with the manifest presence of God. From that moment onward, for all eternity, you are flooded and filled with perfect Love and perfect Peace.

"Eleazer, my heart is filled with joy not sorrow at the thought of dying! I long to look into His eyes, eyes unlike any other, and hear Him say, 'Come, you who are blessed of My Father, inherit the Kingdom prepared for you from the foundation of the world. For I was hungry, and you gave Me something to eat; I was thirsty, and you gave Me something to drink; I was a stranger, and you invited Me in. I was naked, and you clothed Me; I was sick, and you visited Me; I was in prison, and you came to Me.'"[78]

"When was Jesus in prison?" Eleazer asks.

"He is in prison right now, at this moment because many of His loyal friends are in prison. You see, Eleazer, Jesus is a King who identifies in a very real way with the pain and suffering of those in His Kingdom. He relates to each believer to the degree that it is just as if He Himself is sitting in this prison cell. Whatever is done to us is done to Him. Whatever we suffer, He suffers. If we're hungry, He's hungry. If we're beaten, He's beaten. If we rejoice, He rejoices. He feels it all, my brother; He feels it all."[79]

"I've never heard of such a thing. Why would he subject himself to such misery?"

"Because He loves you and me. Eleazer, we do not have a high priest who cannot sympathize with our weakness but One who has been tempted in all things as we are, yet without sin. He cares for you."[80]

"Interesting concept," he replies.

"Eleazer, there is only one thing on this earth that holds any attraction for me now, and that is sharing the Good News with those who do not know Jesus to be the Son of God."

"Peter, if there is any chance that Jesus could heal my weary, miserable soul, then I am willing to listen. You have somehow captured my interest. I am still not fully convinced, but I will listen to what you have to say," Eleazer replies.

"'Tis a wise man that seeks Truth. If you seek Him; you will find Him; that is His promise to you. Now, let's seek Him together, my brother."[81]

CHAPTER SIXTEEN

Even though I loved following Jesus throughout Israel, it always felt good to be on the sea. I looked up at the deep blue skies; the evening stars were making their presence known. The breeze felt good.

I could not stop thinking about how Jesus took five loaves and two fish and fed a multitude.

Matthew was the first to speak saying, "You don't think that they will actually proclaim Him king, do you?"

"It certainly seemed like the people were ready to do exactly that, but Jesus won't let them make Him king," I answered.

"And what makes you say that?" Bartholomew asked.

Before I could respond, Simon the Zealot said, "Look at what Jesus just did—He created food! He took a handful of bread and made thousands and thousands of rolls! From two fish, He fed five thousand men plus women and children! Surely someone who can do something as miraculous as that could deliver us from Rome! Why shouldn't He be made king?"

Judas added, "King David, who was our greatest and

most powerful king, never performed any miracles, did he? I don't think feeding a few people qualifies someone for ruling a nation."

"Feeding a *few*?!" I exclaimed. "Were you too busy counting the coins in the treasury bag to notice the incredible miracle that He performed?"

"I saw, but like I said, king David never did any miracles and look how great he was," Judas answered.

"Regardless, I think Jesus would make a great king," Thomas said.

I quickly added, "Just think of all the miracles we have seen Him perform and the demons He has cast out. And think of all the times the demons confessed Him to be the Son of God. I would certainly fight to make Him king, if He were to give Himself to such a noble thing."

"As would I," Phillip added.

John replied, "Did you not see the look in the Master's eyes? He has no desire to be made king, not now anyway."

"John is right," I added, "He told me before we left that He was going to send the people away because He wasn't ready to be king and He didn't want it to happen that way."

"That means that He plans to be king then?" James questioned.

"That's what it seemed like to me.," I replied.

"The Scribes and Pharisees won't allow it," Judas responded.

"Well, He not only has to deal with the hostility of the Scribes and Pharisees, but now He must deal with the multitudes who see Him as the deliverer of Israel!"

I looked back at the not so distant mountain.

"He could have been king, and we would have been important and rich and powerful," Thomas said, expressing what we were all thinking but were hesitant to say.

I soon fell asleep.

I woke about four in the morning. Because it was a

windless night, we were only about halfway across the sea, which was fine with me. I was thoroughly enjoying the solitude.

Suddenly and without warning, a fierce wind swept across the water. We sprung to our feet and quickly dropped the sails. Within minutes, the moon and stars were obstructed by thick, angry clouds. I searched the sky to determine our exact location but was unable to find a single star.

Contrary headwinds assaulted us, tossing our boat here and there like it was a piece of straw.

"This is going to be a bad one," I yelled.

"Hold on," Andrew shouted.

The sea had suddenly become our greatest enemy; wave after wave crashed over us. After what seemed like hours of fighting the winds and bailing water, we were completely drenched and thoroughly exhausted.

I stopped for a moment to rest my aching arms. Looking across the angry sea, I saw something. At first, I thought it was my imagination, but I quickly realized there was more to it than that. Being both terrified and curious, I dared not take my eyes from the shadowy figure that rapidly approached. The apparition appeared to be walking across the tall waves.

I moved to a different place in the boat, trying to get a better look. John noticed me staring into the darkness and asked, "What is it, Simon?"

"Does anyone see what I see?" I asked, pointing to the figure.

Everyone stopped rowing and peered into the darkness. "I see—something!" Matthew said.

"I see it, too," Judas added.

"It's a ghost!" Thomas cried out in fear.

"It appears to be coming right for us," Andrew shouted as he moved to the other side of the boat.

Terrified, we no longer noticed the wind tossing our boat like a child tosses a coin; we no longer noticed the water filling the bottom, neither did we notice the sea water stinging our faces and arms. All we were aware of was the fact that a ghost seemed to be making its way towards us; fear filled our hearts.

From across the storm-tossed sea, a familiar voice shouted, "Take courage, it is I. Do not be afraid!"

"Does this ghost also have a voice?" Judas cried out ducking behind me.

The apparition paused and then turned away as if to pass us by.

"Master?" I whispered.

Could it be?

I strained to make out His features but could not. Shouting above the roaring wind, I cried out, "Lord, if it is really You, allow me to come to You on the water!"

The shadowy figure immediately turned and said, "Come!"

I wish I could say that it was faith that propelled me out of that boat, but it was nothing of the sort. I simply responded to His invitation out of youthful zeal. My actions were a result of my impetuous, headlong nature and my love for adventure, not that of a heart filled with faith.

I flung my leg over the side of the boat and put my foot on a substance that I had no business walking on except for the fact that the Master bid me come. To my delight, the water supported my weight. Taking a few steps, I looked back over my shoulder at the others who still clung to the sides of the boat. I could hear them shouting, "Simon, who do you think you are? What do you think you are doing? You can't walk on water—that's impossible! Simon, turn around before it's too late!"

I chose to ignore them; I chose to believe.

With my eyes on Jesus, I continued on. The water was

solid under my feet.

This is great! I, Simon, son of John am walking on water!
The winds fought against me, but I kept going.

At some point in my journey, I looked back at the storm-tossed boat; the guys were still shouting, but I could no longer hear them.

Pride filled my heart.

Look at me! I'm walking on water!

A sudden gust of wind nearly knocked me over. The eight-foot high wave looked like the tongue of a sea monster attempting to swallow me up.

Fear took the place of pride and flooded my heart.

I lost sight of the Master.

The sea pulled at my ankles. I looked back at the boat, which was much too far away for me to run to.

"I am not a good swimmer," I shouted into the wind.

My feet started sinking into the deep, dark water. Within seconds, I was waist deep and still sinking. "Lord! Save me!" I shouted.

A hand immediately reached down; I wasted no time taking it. I looked up into the kind eyes of my beloved Friend and Master! He lifted me out of my desperate circumstances and set me on solid ground, which, in this case, happened to be water. Shaking violently, I clung to Jesus as the wind fiercely assailed us. The storm did not seem so formidable with the Master by my side.

As we walked to the boat, Jesus kindly said, "Oh, Peter, such little trust you have. Why did you doubt, My friend? Do you not remember how I stilled the waves and calmed the storm before?"

I did not know how to answer. I promised myself that I would never doubt again.

With peace flooding my heart, I realized that I was still walking on water even if it was with the Master's help. Hope flooded my being; I was not a complete failure.

With head held high, I fell into the boat followed closely by Jesus. Then the strangest thing happened—the wind instantly ceased its assault, and the sea was as smooth as a newly shorn lamb. The clouds quickly fled as though chased by a mighty army. Within minutes, the moon and stars were no longer cloaked in darkness but shone in their fullness. We were greatly astonished. I fell at Jesus' feet, exclaiming, "You are indeed the Son of God!"

He made no reply. I did not need Him to. I now knew the truth; I now knew who He was.[82]

Immediately, our boat went from the middle of the sea to scrubbing its bottom on a rocky beach. I saw, in the early morning light, that instead of being at Bethsaida where Jesus had instructed us to sail, we were at Gennesaret, neighbor to the Gadarenes.

The storm must have blown us off course.

Speaking to my thoughts, Jesus said, "Peter, we are exactly where we are suppose to be."

"Of course we are," I answered quite puzzled.

Jesus fixed His gaze on the shores of Gennesaret. We moored our boat to the shore, and the Master stepped out. Within minutes, the people surrounded Him the way children affectionately gather around their father who has returned from a long journey.

I watched as several men hurried away telling everyone to bring the sick and demonized, for Jesus had come. After alerting their village, they continued on throughout the neighboring districts, announcing the arrival of the Master and inviting all to come.

I was shocked at our warm reception because this was the same country whose people sent us away after Jesus cast out the legion of demons from the two men living in the tombs.

What has caused this dramatic change of heart?

The people laid the sick in the marketplaces begging

Jesus, with much humility, that they might touch the hem of His cloak. As many as touched it were immediately healed.

Watching this, reminded me of the woman, who was also from this very country, who touched the hem of Jesus' garment and was healed of an issue of blood. She, along with the man delivered from the demons, must have told everyone about the Master.

They must be the reason for this wonderful, warm reception.

As Jesus was healing the people, an elderly man addressed me saying, "How is it that Jesus has come here?"

"What do you mean, sir?"

He answered, "The whole town is talking about your arrival, for we received a report from the other side of the sea saying that Jesus' disciples left in the only boat there was, but he stayed behind disappearing on the mountain top."

"It is as you have heard," I answered.

He continued, "They also say that a boat from Tiberias arrived in search of the teacher. They climbed the mountain, but he was no where to be found."

"I believe that to be true," I responded.

"If that be true, and I certainly do not disbelieve your report, then how did he arrive here in your boat?"

"He walked across the water and joined us in the middle of the sea."

"Stop your foolish jesting; I have no time for it, for I am an old man."

"I do not jest, sir. Jesus came to us in the middle of the night, walking on the sea. And not only did He walk on the sea, but He invited me to join Him, which I did."

"I wasn't born yesterday, young man! I do not believe what you say, for it is absolutely impossible to walk on water!"

"But it is true."

"Let us talk of other things," he said as he straightened his drooping shoulders and leaned forward. "I also heard that Jesus fed a large multitude with a handful of bread and fish."

His statement appeared to be more like a question than a statement.

"He did exactly that," I answered.

"News of this miracle has spread far and wide. The people are talking of making Jesus king of Israel," he said.

"That is also true," I answered.

"Jesus may be able to heal sick people and multiply bread, but he will never be king of Israel," he said as he turned away.

"Why do you say that?" I call out after him.

Stopping, he answered, "Everyone knows that he cannot be the king of the Jews, for he is merely a carpenter and the son of a carpenter from Nazareth."

"It is true, what you say, but Jesus has already proven that He can do things that are impossible for others. Who knows, maybe this carpenter from Nazareth will be Israel's new king."

He walked away muttering to himself about foolish, young men.

After teaching the people and healing those who were sick, in order to be back in Capernaum in time for the Sabbath, Jesus bid the people farewell. They pleaded with Him to stay, which was so different from His first visit here.

As we walked down the dusty road toward Capernaum, I looked behind and saw a large crowd following. About an hour into our journey, we were met by a group of men from Judea. Upon recognizing Jesus, they descended on Him like flies on honey and asked, "Teacher, when and how did You get here?"

Jesus answered, "I tell you, you're not looking for Me because you saw miraculous signs but because I fed you bread and your stomachs were full!

"I say to you do not work for food which passes away, but work for the good that remains forever, which the Son of Man will give you, for He is the One on whom God the Father has put His seal."

He continued on, teaching and instructing the people. Having arrived in Capernaum, we immediately went to the synagogue. The same men who had encountered Jesus on the road, came to Him and asked, "What shall we do, that we may do the works of God?"

Jesus answered, "This is the work of God, that you believe in Him whom He has sent."

"What miracle will you do for us that we may see it and trust You? What works can you perform? Can you do what Moses did? Our fathers ate manna in the desert, just as it says in the Law, 'He gave them bread out of heaven to eat.' We know that you fed the multitude with only five loaves and two fishes, but are you able to do what Moses did?"

Jesus answered, "Truly, truly I say to you that it was not Moses who gave you the bread out of heaven."

His statement caused a great disturbance among the people, for Moses is sacred to the Jewish people.

Jesus is treading on dangerous ground.

He continued, "Truly, truly I say to you that it is My Father who gives you the true bread out of heaven. For the bread of God is that which comes down out of heaven and gives life to the world."

A man shouted out, "Lord, evermore give us this bread! Feed us as You did on the hillside!"

Jesus responded, "I am the bread, which is life! Whoever comes to Me will never go hungry, and whoever trusts in Me will never be thirsty. You have seen Me, but you still do not believe."

"What kind of bread satisfies hunger in such a way that one is never hungry again?" a man asked.

"The bread of life," Jesus answered.

"Give this bread," the man responded.

"Everyone the Father gives Me will come to Me, and whoever comes to Me I will certainly not turn away. For I have come down from heaven not to do My will, but the will of the One who sent Me. And this is the will of the One who sent Me: that I should not lose any of those He has given Me but should raise them up on the Last Day. This is the will of My Father that all who see the Son and trust in Him should have eternal life, and I will raise them up Myself on the last day."

A great dispute broke out among those who had been following Jesus. Many walked away grumbling because He claimed to be the bread that came down from heaven. Even among those who stayed with Him there was great dissension. An argument suddenly broke out as one man said, "Isn't this Jesus, the son of Joseph, whose father and mother we know?"

Another answered, "It is indeed."

"Then how is it that he claims to have come down out of heaven?"

"How dare he claim to be anything other than the son of Mary and Joseph!'" an elderly man shouted.

Jesus interrupted them, saying, "Stop grumbling and arguing among yourselves. No one can come to Me, unless the Father, the One who sent Me, draws him, and I will raise him up on the Last Day. It is written in the Prophets, 'They will all be taught of God.'

"Everyone who listens to the Father and learns from Him comes to Me. Not that anyone has seen the Father except the One who is from God—He has seen the Father. Yes, indeed! I tell you, whoever trusts in Me has eternal life; I am the bread which is life. Your fathers ate the manna in the desert, and they died. But, the bread that comes down from heaven is such that a person may eat it and not die.

"I am the living bread that has come down from heaven; if anyone eats this bread, he will live forever. Furthermore, the bread that I will give is My own flesh, and I will give it for the life of the world."

Hearing this, the men disputed among themselves saying, "How can this man give us his flesh to eat? It is against the Law to eat human flesh!"

Responding to their debate, Jesus said, "Truly, truly, I tell You that unless you eat the flesh of the Son of Man and drink His blood, you do not have life in yourselves. Whoever eats My flesh and drinks My blood has eternal life, which means that I will raise him up on the Last Day. For My flesh is true food, and My blood is true drink. Whoever eats My flesh and drinks My blood lives in Me and I live in him. Just as the living Father sent Me, and I live through the Father, so also whoever eats My flesh will live through Me.

"So, this is the bread that has come down from heaven. It is not like the bread your fathers ate, for they ate and still died, but whoever eats this bread will live forever!"

"What?! How dare you tell us to do such a revolting thing!" a man shouted.

Many others joined in the verbal assault of Jesus. Without saying another word, Jesus led us out of the synagogue. Several men who had been a disciple of His for over a year ran up to Him and asked Him, "What you said back there about eating your flesh, that is a difficult statement to understand; therefore, we can not accept it. Who can bear to listen to it?"

Jesus responded, "Does this cause you to stumble? If something as small as this causes you to stumble, then what will you do if you should behold the Son of Man ascending to the place He was before?"

They made no answer. But then, how could they, for who could understand what He was saying? I certainly did not.

Jesus continued, "It is the Spirit who gives life, and without the Spirit physical things have no value. The words I have spoken to you are Spirit and life, yet some among you do not believe. This is why I told you that no one can come to Me unless the Father has granted it."

At this point, a great debate broke out, which resulted in more of His disciples announcing that they would no longer follow Him. I watched as many turned their backs on the Master and walked away.

Jesus was deeply affected by the sight of so many deciding to exchange eternal life for the empty, temporal things this world offers. His face was etched with grief as they walked away from the One who loved them more than life itself.

With a deep sigh, Jesus led us on in silence. We had gone only a short distance when He stopped. Turning to the twelve of us, He asked, "You do not wish to go away too, do you?"

If words had a physical substance, my heart would have been cut in two pieces. I looked into His dark brown eyes and saw a depth of pain greater than anything I had ever seen.

Where else could I go? John the Baptist is dead, and even if he were alive, he would send me to Jesus. I could never go back to the Scribes and Pharisees, for Jesus has exposed the shallowness, hypocrisy and pride that their religion is steeped in. He has shown me what religion without relationship looks like, and it is repulsive. If I go to the Sadducees, I am ruined, for they say that there is no resurrection and idolize the material things of this earth. I cannot follow the multitude, for they wander here and there in search of a deliverer who will set them free from Roman bondage.

Jesus is the only One with words of eternal life. He is the only One I desire to follow, for His character and nature are flawless, holy and pure. My intellect may be challenged, but my heart is fixed on Him! There is absolutely no where else to go!

Looking up I answered, "Lord, to whom shall we go? You have words of eternal life, and we have believed and come to know that You are the Holy One of God."

Jesus answered, "You believe, but I chose the twelve of you, and yet, one of you is a traitor."[83]

What, a traitor among us?

I looked around.

Who would dare to betray the Lord?

It was one thing for the multitude to turn their backs on the Lord, but to have a traitor in our midst was unthinkable. We had been together for almost two years, and I could not imagine that any of us would do such a thing. We all knew that Judas helped himself to the money bag from time to time, but that was far from being a traitor. Surely, the Lord meant something else. This must be one of those mysterious sayings that He was famous for.

I quickly put His words out of my mind.

I could not understand what possible connection there could be between eating His flesh and eternal life, but I had come to love this Man and had come to believe that He was sent from God. His message was strange, difficult to understand and even repulsive to my Jewish upbringing, but I believed in Him.

"Jesus, I understand that the people were offended with Your message, but why must they leave?" I asked.

"The people are not so much offended with My message as they are with Me. You see, Peter, I am not the man they thought I was. They saw Me multiply the bread and dreamed of a king who would fill their stomachs, meet their expectations and provide them with earthly comfort and provisions so that they could live a life of idleness, plenty and pleasure. But, that is not why I have come," Jesus responded.

"Tell me, why did You come?" I asked.

"I came because of love, Peter."

CHAPTER SEVENTEEN

Laban exclaims, "A traitor! Was it true? Was one of the apostles a traitor?"

"I am sad to say that it was true."

"Who was it? Who could do such a thing?" Laban asks.

"Denying the Lord is not as difficult as you might suppose if there is selfish ambition or pride in your heart," I answer remembering my own personal denial of the Lord.

Eleazer interrupts, "Peter, you have not helped your cause in relating this story to me. You have certainly turned me against believing that your teacher could ever be who you claim him to be. The true Messiah would never tell people to eat his flesh and drink his blood, for that is clearly forbidden! How absurd! How disgusting! The man who would dare speak in such a manner is either a lunatic or a fool, or both. This Jesus of Nazareth cannot be the Messiah, for the Messiah would never instruct Jewish men to do something that is such a clear transgression of the Law!"

"You misunderstand what Jesus was saying, my brother and friend. Let me explain. The Passover was near, which was the time when the Passover lamb was sacrificed and then eaten. In telling us to eat His flesh and drink His blood, Jesus was saying, 'I am the true Passover Lamb. The bread that I will give is My body sacrificed on a cross— it is My body, which I will lay down for the life of the world.'

"Eleazer, Jesus was speaking with His cross in clear sight, for that is where He gave Himself as a sacrifice. He was speaking of what was to come. The test was whether or not the people would accept Jesus as the Messiah, not follow Him because of the food that He might provide or the miracles that He could do.

"The multitude had just seen Jesus feed thousands with five loaves and two fish. But, their accusation was that Jesus' miracle was nothing in comparison to Moses' feeding a whole nation with manna from heaven.

"Jesus pointed out the fact that the manna Moses fed Israel had no power to prevent death, but that Jesus was the true Bread, which is capable of destroying death and grants to those who receive it the free gift of eternal life."

Eleazer interrupts, "Do you mean to say that the flesh and blood of Jesus is the source of eternal life? Are you comparing Jesus to the tree of life in the garden of Eden, which offered eternal life?"

"That is exactly what I am saying."

"Tell me then, how is this bread to be appropriated?" Eleazer asks.

"To eat is to believe and receive Jesus as the Son of God, the Messiah. Jesus once said, 'He that comes to Me shall never hunger, and he that believes in Me shall never thirst.'[84]

"Our Jewish brothers asked Jesus for a sign greater than His feeding of the multitude. Jesus did eventually give them a sign, but not at all what they wanted or expected. The sign that He gave was His death on the cross and His resurrection from the grave three days later. Jesus' life, death and resurrection did indeed become food and drink for all who desire eternal life."

Eleazer is silent. I wait and silently pray.

"So," Eleazer asks, "you saw Him die, but did you also see Him after He rose from the dead?"

"Like I said before, I did see Jesus after His resurrection. I actually ran away when Jesus was arrested, which is another story. But, I did see Him with my own eyes, as did many others after He rose from the grave."

"How do you know He was really dead then?"

"I know because John followed Jesus to the cross and remained there with Jesus' mother until His death," I respond.

"Perhaps, I should desire to eat this bread? What would you say to that?" Eleazer asks.

"I would say, 'Praise God!' for to do so is the beginning of life eternal. Do you believe that Jesus is the Son of God? Are you ready to acknowledge Jesus as the Lamb of God who was slain for your sins?"

"I have never needed anyone or anything, but something grips my heart and won't let me go, something good and kind and compelling. For the first time in my life, I feel as though I am in dire need. I fear that I will perish without this bread. My cold, hard, calloused heart is in great agony, and my mind is in great turmoil," Eleazer states.

"Then surrender your life to Jesus and receive His forgiveness for your sins," I answer.

"Is it really that easy?"

"It is."

"Peter, there is a war raging within me. Part of me wants to hold onto my hatred, anger and bitterness, while another part is exhausted and longs for peace. I cannot continue in this state of perpetual conflict. I must know Him! Someone set me free from this prison of sin!"

"There is only One who can grant you the freedom that you need, Eleazer and it is Jesus Christ, the Son of God.

Give Him your sinful heart in exchange for His perfect one. Are you ready to surrender and allow the King to transform you by the power of His death on the cross?"

"I am," Eleazer states.

"Then tell Him. Confess that you are a sinner in need of a Savior. Ask Him to forgive you for your sins and wash you white as snow. Tell Him that you receive His free gift of eternal life and desire to be a part of His kingdom. Talk to Him, Eleazer, for He is waiting and longing for you to do so."

I silently pray while waiting.

Eleazer finally whispers, "Jesus, I confess that I am a sinner in need of a Savior. I ask You to forgive me for my many sins, especially for murdering my neighbor and creating so much destruction and pain for his family and mine."

Eleazer breaks down sobbing. I hear Justus, Josiah and Laban quietly praying.

A short time later, Eleazer continues, "And I receive Your free gift of eternal life, Jesus. I want to belong to Your Kingdom not the kingdom of this world or of my own making."

Unable to contain my excitement, I lift my voice in song. After several choruses, my fellow prisoners join in.

There is no greater joy than seeing a life surrendered to the King of kings!

The clanging of keys brings our singing to an abrupt halt. I whisper a prayer, "Oh, Father, not yet. Give us more time."

Passing his torch to a man who remains just outside the doorway, a Roman guard I have never seen before enters. His gruff, angry voice fills our cell, "Was that singing I heard?"

Not waiting for an answer, he kicks each one of us.

Stopping beside Eleazer, he laughs saying, "I guess

this is your lucky day, for I have decided, out of the goodness of my heart, not to beat that song out of you!"

Grabbing Eleazer by the hair of his head, he continues, "You pigs aren't worth the effort."

The guard pulls Eleazer's hair causing his head to be stretched as far as possible. Their faces are just a few inches away; spittle flies from his mouth onto Eleazer's face. The guard says, "You are a stinking Jew, aren't you? I hate Jews almost as much as I hate Christians!"

Eleazer closes his eyes.

Oh, Lord, please help him remain silent. Send help now, Lord, I pray!

The guard spews out a long string of curse words. He jerks Eleazer's head back and continues, "But, as I said, you aren't worth the effort!"

He slams Eleazer's face against the post and spins around on his heel. "What are you staring at?" he angrily asks.

Before I can respond, he grabs me by the hair and says, "You are a filthy, stinking Jewish pig, too!"

I see it coming and brace myself as his fist lands squarely across my jaw. Between clenched teeth, he says, "If it was up to me, I would kill you myself, but Nero has left strict instructions that you are not to die until he can personally enjoy the entertainment."

The guard then says, "But, the real reason I am here is to end the life of Justus, son of Aristochus."

Without a moment's hesitation, Justus answers, "I am the one you are looking for."

"Today is your special day, for it is the day you will die. It has recently come to our attention that you are a follower of Jesus, the false prophet. Is that true?"

"It is true that I am a follower of Jesus, but it is not true that He is a false prophet."

"Then you will not only die for the crimes you have

committed, but also for being a fool," he says, laughing.

"You may kill my body, but I will live forever," Justus states confidently.

Standing over him like a vulture claims its prey, he replies, "You stinking fool!"

The guard unlocks the chains around Justus's ankles. Justus looks up at me; I am thankful for the dim light. His face is full of peace and even joy. He smiles, nodding slightly. I return his smile as tears fill my eyes.

Laban calls out, "Justus, my friend, I will pray for you."

"As will I," Josiah says.

"Pray all you want, but your prayers won't change this man's fate," the guard states.

He then yanks Justus to his feet, but Justus immediately collapses. Landing in a heap, he says, "My legs were both broken during my arrest, and I have not been able to stand since that day."

"Did I ask you a question?" the guard shouts kicking him roughly in the side.

Not waiting for Justus to catch his breath, he grabs his chain and drags him across the filthy, stone floor.

As he passes by, I get a close look at Justus's face. He looks to be not more than twenty years of age. He smiles and says, "Thank you, Peter, for today I will be with Jesus! I only regret that I cannot hear more—."

"Shut-up!" the guard shouts stopping to kick him in the ribs.

Justus groans in pain.

"Justus, remember the Lord!" I shout.

"Shut-up, or I will take you instead of him!" the guard shouts.

"I am ready to die in his place," I respond.

Ignoring me, he continues on. The heavy iron door slams shut behind them. The only sound is that of the chains being dragged across the stone hallway and the cursing of the guard.

I silently pray for Justus to remain true unto death and for the God of all comfort to be with him. I hear Josiah and Laban praying as well.

"Peter?"

"Yes, Eleazer?"

"What can I do?" he asks.

"You can pray. Jesus may be seated in heaven, but His eyes move to and fro throughout the earth strongly supporting those whose hearts are completely His," I answer.[85]

"But, I am not sure exactly how to pray. What if I get it wrong?"

"Praying is simply talking to God just as you would to a friend. Tell Him what you want, what you feel, what you need Him to do," I answer.

Eleazer is silent; I return to my prayers. Before long, I hear Eleazer sobbing. I whisper, "That is one of the best ways to pray, my friend."

Not long afterward, the sound of footsteps causes us to hold our breath. A fist pounds on our door, and a voice exclaims, "Your Christian friend no longer lives!"

His sick laughter causes my stomach to turn.

I can do nothing but weep.

Eleazer suddenly bursts out, "Is there any comfort? Is there any hope? Is there really life after death?"

I respond, "Eleazer, I do not weep for Justus, for he is now free. He is dressed in a white robe, wearing a martyr's crown, standing face to face with the King of all kings. Neither do I weep for despair, but I weep for that guard who is without hope and destined to spend eternity in hell should he not embrace the King.

"As for hope and comfort, we will never run out of either as long as we know the King. Oh, my friend, there is all the more hope and comfort for Justus now that he is with

Jesus. Justus is more alive now than he ever was. He is free, and he is with the Lord where there is no sorrow nor suffering. He is rejoicing, my friend," I answer.

Eleazer does not respond.

"Eleazer, you took quite a blow to your face. What is the extent of the damage?" I ask.

"It is nothing that won't heal," he answers.

Somewhere down the hall a door is unlocked, and the sound of angry voices fill the hall. Within minutes, the sound of a whip cracking through the air causes me to focus my prayers on the poor soul at the end of that guard's untamed fury. I pray until I fall asleep.

I sleep, for how long, I do not know. I wake to the sound of Eleazer asking, "Is anyone awake?"

"I am," Josiah quietly responds.

"As am I," Laban adds.

"I, too, am awake," I answer clearing my throat.

"I must admit that I am shaken to the core. I can't sleep for thinking about Justus. I have wasted my entire life on things that mean absolutely nothing. It is strange how one's perspective changes when coming face to face with death. That door could open at any time, and my life could end. I know now that I am not ready. I believe that Jesus is the Messiah, but I do not love Him the way He deserves to be loved, considering the price He paid for me.

"I know that there is more, and I must have it. I need to have my heart transformed and strengthened before I die. Tell me more, Peter, tell me more about this Jesus, this King of the Jews!" Eleazer pleads.

I stretch my neck trying to alleviate the pain that racks my head, neck and back. I answer, "Eleazer, you are right; there is more. Christianity is a journey into the very heart of God. I will tell you more, but first, I must find out how Josiah and Laban are."

"I, too, am shaken," Josiah answers, "I would be lying

if I said that I am not affected by Justus's death. He was my friend. I keep reminding myself that this isn't the end of his life but merely the beginning, but still I am undone."

"And you, Laban? How are you, my friend?"

"I thought that I would be the first to die since I was arrested before all of you. My heart is at peace even though my friend is gone. It is strange, but I find myself feeling a bit jealous that Justus got to die first," Laban states.

"Peter, take our minds off of this tragedy and tell us more about Jesus," Eleazer pleads.

Laban adds, "Peter, that would be best. You stopped at the part where Jesus asked the twelve of you if you were going to leave Him like so many others had."

"I am constantly amazed at how well you remember what I have said," I respond.

"That is because our priorities have changed due to the fact that life, as we know it, is about to end. Jesus has now become the center of my existence," Laban responds.

Eleazer interrupts, "I don't mean to be rude, but could we just get on with it? I am painfully aware of how little time I may have and how little I know about my newly discovered Savior!"

Greatly encouraged over Eleazer's hunger, I continue, "What we didn't realize at the time was that Jesus deliberately delivered that message about eating His flesh for the purpose of separating the true disciples from the false ones just as the wind separates the chaff from a kernel of wheat.

"Many were offended, but those who remained were hungry for the truth. It became increasingly clear that Jesus was not a puppet on a string, neither was He willing to promote their agendas or feed their fleshly appetites. From the time He delivered that message about eating His flesh and drinking His blood, His popularity declined immediately and drastically, but it concerned Him not.

Jesus was not a Man who was seeking to win a popularity contest neither was He interested in gaining the approval of man. He desired only one thing, and that was to fulfill the will of His Father in heaven."

CHAPTER EIGHTEEN

After watching so many of His followers turn away, Jesus remained in Galilee and refused to go to Judea because He knew that the Jews were seeking to kill Him.

A group of Scribes and Pharisees had made the nearly one-hundred-mile journey from Jerusalem in an attempt to catch Jesus in some offense that they could use to accuse Him. They followed us everywhere we went, watching all that He did and listening to every word He said.

At the end of a long day, hungry and exhausted, we made our way to the house where we were staying. We collapsed around the table and quickly devoured the delicious food. The Scribes and Pharisees, in their flowing robes and tassels and phylacteries, looked on.

Having finished eating, one of them addressed Jesus and asked, "Why is it that Your disciples break the tradition of the Elders by eating with unclean hands?"

The Pharisees, as do most Jewish men, hold fast to the tradition of the Elders and do not eat unless they have carefully washed their hands. To fail to do so was not just a matter of bad manners and uncleanliness, but to them it was a matter of being unclean in God's sight. According to the Scribes and Pharisees, observing the traditions of their fathers is how one pleases God; to break them is sin.

Jesus answered, "And why do you yourselves transgress the commandment of God for the sake of your tradition? For God said, 'Honor your father and mother,' and, 'He who speaks evil of father or mother, let him be put to death.'

"But you teach them to say to their parents, 'Anything of mine that you might have been helped with has been given to God.'

"In doing so, they cannot help their father or mother, thus invalidating the word of God by your tradition which has been handed down. You do many things such as that. You put your traditions before what is right and necessary.

"You hypocrites, rightly did Isaiah prophesy of you, saying, 'This people honors me with their lips, but their heart is far from Me. In vain, they worship Me, teaching as doctrines the precepts of men.'

"You hold to the tradition of men while neglecting the commandments of God, and you have made a fine art of it!"

Jesus then turned away from them and addressed those gathered in the house saying, "Listen to Me, all of you and understand. There is nothing outside the man which going into him can defile him, but the things which proceed out of the man are what defile the man.

"If any man has ears to hear, let him hear."

The following day, Jesus moved among the people while the Scribes and Pharisees followed closely behind. As we walked, I came alongside Jesus and asked, "Do you know that the Pharisees were offended by your statement last night?"

Stopping to look at me, He answered, "Every plant

which My heavenly Father did not plant shall be rooted up."

Once again, His message is strange and difficult to understand. Why must He always speak in riddles?

"Peter, do not worry about the Scribes and Pharisees; let them alone. They are blind guides of the blind, and if a blind man guides a blind man, both will fall into a pit."

I laid my hand on Jesus' shoulder and said, "Master, I do not understand. Did not God Himself give us a long list of animals that are unclean and may not be eaten? How can You say that nothing that goes into a man from the outside can render him unclean? Because of the Law, there are many Jews throughout history who chose to die rather than eat meat that was unclean."

"Oh, Peter, are you still lacking in understanding also? Do you not see that nothing going into a person from the outside can make him unclean in respect to his spiritual state? For it doesn't go into his heart but into his stomach, and then passes out of the body. It is what comes out of a person that makes him unclean. For from within, out of a person's heart, comes wicked thoughts, sexual immorality, theft, murder, adultery, greed, malice, deceit, indecency, envy, slander, arrogance and foolishness. All these wicked things come from within, and that is what makes a person unclean."

I am shocked by His answer. Jesus, in one stroke, just wiped out a Law that many Jews throughout history had died for!

He is saying that cleanliness has nothing to do with what people eat but everything to do with what comes out of their hearts! By saying this, Jesus is declaring all meats to be clean! Unbelievable!

That night, I laid under the stars unable to sleep because of the tremendous stirring in my heart.

How does Jesus divide between soul and Spirit with such

kindness and humility? Never has there been a Man so meek
and humble as Jesus. He gives Himself so sacrificially to
those who mistreat Him and use Him for their own selfish
gain? How does He respond with love to those who accuse
Him so viciously? How does He persevere under such railings
and selfish demands?

The only answer I have is that Jesus is so much more
than a man; He truly is the Son of God and is perfectly able
to love unconditionally.

Never had a man been so talked about as Jesus was in
Galilee. Controversy, debate and testing surrounded Him
on every side.

Because of the constant demands of the crowds, I was
relieved when Jesus announced that as soon as the
Sabbath was complete, we would be leaving Galilee.

Perhaps, we will finally have a respite from the crowds
and their numerous opinions.[86]

To my delight, we left early Sunday morning, and after
a relatively short journey, we arrived on the borders of
Tyre and Sidon. We stayed in a Jewish home just on the
Galilean border because Tyre and Sidon were pagan cities,
Gentile territories and none of us apostles relished the
thoughts of spending time there.

Even though I had been raised to despise and even
hate Gentiles, I was glad to be here because in this place
Jesus was, for the most part, unknown, which meant that
there were no crowds to fight with, no Pharisees to harass
us and no sick people asking to be healed.

The following morning, as we reclined around the
breakfast table, Jesus said, "Tell no one who I am."

I leaned over to John and whispered, "One may hide a
candle for a short time, but no one can hide the sun."

For the next three days, we sat at Jesus' feet. On the
morning of the fourth day, as we walked through the
Galilean countryside enjoying the Master's undivided

attention, I announced, "Jesus, it has been good to be here with You."

"I agree," added John throwing his arm over Jesus' shoulder.

Jesus responded, "To you it is given to know the mysteries of heaven."

James said, "Master, I will follow You wherever You go."

Our peaceful walk was suddenly interrupted by the sound of a woman yelling in the distance.

At least we had three glorious days alone with Jesus before the inevitable happened.

The woman was running towards us, her arms waving wildly in an attempt to gain our attention. Jesus stopped to watch her fast approach. "Come, Lord, let us go from here," I said slightly tugging on His arm.

He resisted me, saying, "This is a Gentile woman of Greek origin."

"Even more reason to leave," I responded, having no desire to have our privacy interrupted.

"No, Simon," He answered, "She is a woman of great faith."

How does He know that?

Seeing His determination to encounter this woman, I removed my hand. The woman increased her speed, all the while crying out in a loud voice, "Have mercy on me, oh Lord, Son of David! Have mercy, for my daughter is cruelly demon possessed!"

The Master offered no response. Surprised, I looked at Him. His face communicated nothing. He turned around and walked away.

This is certainly unusual behavior, quite contrary to His normal attentive, compassionate ways. What is He doing and why?

The woman was undaunted by the Master's seeming

disinterest. The twelve of us quickly gathered around Jesus in a desperate attempt to hide and protect Him from this Gentile. But, it merely caused the woman to shout all the more.

I motioned for her to go away, but she ignored me.

Jesus walked on as if she did not exist.

If He's not going to intervene, He should send her away.

The desperate woman shouted after the Master. She pushed her way between James and me. Grabbing her arm, I said, "Jesus, would You please send this woman away, for she keeps shouting out after us."

Jesus turned to me and answered, "I was sent only to the lost sheep of the house of Israel."

Fine, then why don't You send her away?

The woman heard His response and cried out even more. Breaking free from my grip, she threw herself on the ground before Him and grabbed His ankle pleading, "Lord, help me!"

With great gentleness He responded, "Let the children be fed first, for it is not right to take the children's bread and give it to the dogs that eat from the Master's table."

She slowly sat up; He walked away.

Scrambling to her feet, she quickly followed saying, "Lord, I know that what You say is true, but the Master's pets are never denied the crumbs. These well-loved animals are even given a place under the Master's table where they eagerly wait for the bread that his children clean their hands on and then throw away."

The Master smiled.

Once again, she fell at His feet. Clutching the hem of His garment, she continued, "I ask not for a loaf or a morsel, only for a crumb. Oh, please do not deny me this small thing!"

Here is a woman that will not take no for an answer! She, a woman and a Gentile woman at that, clings to the

Master, the bread of heaven, which many of my fellow Jews have rejected and thrown away.

Jesus warmly responded, "O woman, your faith is great! For such an answer you may go home; the demon has left your daughter."

With a shout, the woman jumped to her feet, thanking Him profusely. She then ran away, waving her arms and praising God in a loud voice.

As we walked along the path that led back to the house, I said, "Master, once more I see that You extend mercy to those who are not Jews, even though I do not understand why."

"The Son of Man is not willing for any to perish, but that *all* should come to salvation," He answered.[87]

What does He mean by this statement? Surely, He is not considering including all men in the salvation of Israel? This would be a rude shock to the rulers and people of Israel—a shock that would turn our world upside down and shake the very foundations of our faith, ultimately bringing an end to Judaism as we know it.

"Peter, that woman desired the living Bread, and she was not to be denied," Jesus added.

Could it be that He has brought us here to demonstrate to us that there is no distinction between Jew and Gentile, between clean and unclean people? If so, what a strange concept! One that I am not sure I can embrace.[88]

As I pondered these things, Jesus began singing a song of worship. John pulled out his flute and joined in. Andrew and Thomas quickly added their tambourines. It was not long before we were all dancing and singing as we made our way to the house.

Just as we stepped through the door, Jesus announced that it was time to leave. I gathered my few belongings but could not stop thinking about the events of the day.

Did Jesus bring us here so that He could encounter this

solitary woman, and having accomplished His deed, we are now free to leave? It certainly appears to be the case. But, why would He go so far out of His way for one woman and a Gentile woman, at that? I still don't understand His infinite mercy and unprejudiced compassion for those who are not God's chosen people. It is indeed a mystery to me.

We left the village as the setting sun painted the sky a golden red and orange color.

For the next eight months, we traveled through the territory of Sidon into the country of Phillip the Tetrarch. From there, we continued through the midst of the borders of Decapolis until we reached the southeastern shore of the sea of Galilee where Jesus led us up the mountain. Even though we were within the territory of ancient Israel, these areas were primarily made up of Gentile heathens.

Great multitudes came to Him there. Having received reports of the great Miracle Worker, the people brought those who were sick and plagued with infirmities and laid them at His feet. Jesus healed them all, which resulted in these people glorifying the God of Israel.

I found it difficult to believe that God was visiting these Gentiles, these heathens, in the same way that He visited God's chosen people, the Jews, but there was no way I could deny it.

As Jesus walked among them, shouts of joy filled the air. What a strange sight it was to see the people glorifying the God of Israel, even if they were mostly Gentiles![89]

As we traveled on, a deaf man who could barely speak was brought to Jesus. Placing His arm around the man's shoulder, Jesus led him away from the crowd to a private place. Curious, I followed as did the other apostles.

Jesus put His fingers into the man's ears for a moment, and the man's expression changed instantly. His eyes grew wide, and he grabbed his ears, muttering something that was completely unintelligible.

"Stick out your tongue," Jesus said. Spitting on His fingertips, Jesus placed His saliva on the man's tongue. He then looked up to heaven and groaned deeply. The man stood with his tongue hanging out. Jesus then commanded, "Be opened!"

Immediately, the man began to speak clearly shouting, "I can hear! I can speak! I can both hear and speak!"

In a sudden outburst of emotion, he grabbed Jesus, picked Him up and spun Him around, laughing and crying at the same time. I stepped forward to intervene, but stopped as I realized that Jesus was actually enjoying the man's childlike outburst. After nearly toppling over, the man set Jesus back on His feet. Both men were filled with joy. Jesus threw His arm around the man's shoulder and embraced him tightly. Leaning close, He said to him, "Make sure you tell no one what I have done for you."

With a nod and an aggressive embrace, the man ran directly into the center of the multitude, shouting and praising God. The faces of the people revealed the depth of their amazement; they were as astonished as I was.

The news of Jesus' healing power spread like wildfire. Everywhere we went the people were proclaiming, "Everything Jesus does, He does well! He even makes the deaf to hear and the dumb to speak!"[90]

Jesus comes bringing healing to the sick, freedom to the demonized and salvation to human souls. His deeds are so great that it is as if He has begun the work of creation all over again.

The following morning, while it was still dark, Jesus woke us saying, "Let us go from here to Galilee."

Wasting no time, we gathered our few belongings and followed as did a very large number of those He had taught and healed.

As we traveled on, many joined us. By the third day, there was quite a multitude following this Man from Galilee.

The unpopular Jesus has suddenly become popular again.

We arrived in Decapolis on the fourth day. Jesus called us to His side. Looking across the sea of people, He said, "I feel great compassion for the multitude, for they have been with us for three days now and have had nothing to eat. I do not wish to send them away hungry lest they faint on the way, for some of them have come from a long distance."

Stammering, I answered, "But how, where would we get enough bread in this remote place to satisfy such a great multitude?"

Jesus responded, "How many loaves do you have?"

We quickly counted and answered, "Seven."

"It is more than enough," He responded.

What does He mean? These loaves would only feed three men at the most, and there are thousands here.

With a nod, Jesus directed the multitude to sit on the ground. As they were doing so, Jesus turned back to us and said, "Bring me the bread."

Judas handed the basket of loaves to Jesus. Lifting it before heaven, He gave thanks.

I looked at John. His dark brown eyes were filled with childlike wonder as he stood with his hands open, obviously expecting them to be filled.

He's going to multiply the bread as He did before; I should have known that He would do this!

The Master lowered the basket in John's hands and took out a loaf. With a smile, He broke it, handing half to Thomas and the other half to Matthew.

I should have expected it and even asked Him to do so, considering the fact that He fed five thousand Jewish men with just two fish and five loaves!

Jesus continued to break the loaves and give them to us to pass out. A little boy, no more than seven years of age, ran up to Jesus and said, "My mother said that You could have our fish."

Thanking him, Jesus took the small basket, which held a handful of fish, lifted it to heaven and gave thanks.

Jesus then handed us the fish along with the bread, which enabled us to feed a very hungry multitude made up primarily of Gentiles.

Everyone ate, including us. Once the multitude was satisfied, Jesus said, "Go and pick up the pieces that are left over."

Scouring the crowds, we gathered the remaining food. To our astonishment, there were seven large baskets filled with leftovers!

Standing before Him in utter amazement, Jesus smiled and asked, "Do you not yet understand?"

We could not respond.

Jesus then joined a group of children playing chase nearby. I watched and wondered.

Did Jesus come to satisfy the hunger of both the Jew and the Gentile? Has He come to bring reconciliation and salvation to both? I find it difficult to believe that this could be true. There must be some other explanation for His behavior towards these Gentiles. Perhaps, it means nothing. Perhaps, He merely felt sorry for them. But somehow I do not think so.

Doing a quick head count, John and Judas determined that there were about four thousand men who ate, not counting women and children.

Impossible!

I spun around and looked at Jesus who had become a human tree as little ones climbed all over Him. He returned my gaze as the setting sun bathed Him from head to toe in its rose-colored light. Jesus smiled and then saluted me with a piece of bread.

He never ceased to amaze me, this meek yet absolutely

confident Teacher of Israel! He possessed such love, such kindness, such truth and such indisputable, impeccable integrity.

It was not until many years later that I understood that the feeding of the thousands of Jews was a prophetic sign of the coming of the Bread of God to the Jews. And the feeding of the thousands of Gentiles was a prophetic sign of the coming of the Bread of God to the Gentiles.

The following day, Jesus dismissed the multitudes to return to their homes. He then turned to us and said, "We are going to the region of Magadan, to the district of Dalmanutha."

Climbing into the boat, I wondered what new thing was on the horizon.[91]

CHAPTER NINETEEN

The distant clanging of chains causes me to stop and pray. From the sound, it appears that a large number of prisoners are being herded like cattle past our door. Angry guards shout obscenities at their helpless prisoners.

Oh, Father, have mercy on these guards and protect, strengthen and help those in chains. Reveal Yourself to each of them, I pray.

The sound fades in the distance, but I continue to pray knowing the horrific conditions that await those who find themselves at the mercy of their caretakers.

My heart skips a beat as the door to our cell opens. Malchus quickly identifies himself. I respond, "My brother, I am so glad it is you."

With great urgency, Malchus replies, "Nero has issued an order for ten Christians to be stripped naked and left outside in the bitter cold until they renounce Jesus, and if they refuse, they are to be left exposed to the elements until they die. They have just been led out. Please pray for these men and women. Oh, how they will need the grace of God!"

"Is my wife among them?" I ask.

"I am happy to report that she is not," Malchus answers.

"And what of Paul? Is he among them?"

"He is not," Malchus replies, "I have come to ask for your prayers on their behalf. They will need supernatural strength and courage and grace to see them through this night.

"I must hurry, for I have been assigned to be one of the guards, which is both sweet and bitter. Sweet because I will be able to stand with them and pray, but bitter because I will have to watch my brothers and sisters in Christ suffer a painful death should the Lord not intervene on their behalf."

"We will pray for them and also for you," I answer.

Malchus shuts the door as quietly as possible. I pray as his steps fade away into the darkness.

"Peter, why must following Jesus be so painful?" Eleazer asks.

"My friends, you know that I have been in this prison for more than nine months. On several occasions, I have gone without water and food for so many days that I should have died. I have been beaten so badly that, had God not strengthened me and healed me, I would not be here today. I have endured much at the hands of men, but I consider it pure joy when I face trials and persecutions, knowing that the testing of my faith produces endurance, perseverance and godly character. Suffering is a blessing and a tool in our Father's hand, if we will only respond correctly to it and allow it to have its perfect way."[92]

The sound of someone loudly singing makes its way down the corridor. I listen closely and soon recognize the song. It is a song Paul wrote on one of his missionary journeys.

"Malchus has obviously asked Paul to pray as well," I

say with a smile. With Paul's song as the backdrop, I pray David's ninety-first psalm:

> "Father, these men dwell in Your shelter;
> therefore, they will abide in the shadow of
> the Almighty. You are their refuge and their
> fortress. You are the One they put their
> trust in! It is You who delivers from the
> snare of the trapper and from the deadly
> pestilence. Cover them with Your pinions
> and cause them to seek refuge under Your
> wings. Your faithfulness is a shield and
> bulwark. Therefore, they will not be afraid
> of the terror by night or of the arrows that
> fly by day, of the pestilence that stalks in
> darkness or of the destruction that lays
> waste at noon. A thousand may fall at their
> side and ten thousand at Your right hand,
> but they shall remain untouched by it.
> Father, give Your angels charge concerning
> them, and guard them throughout the night."[93]

Several voices have now joined Paul's. Their song echoes through the hall and invades every cell.

Father, let Your word run swiftly and be glorified throughout this prison, convicting and saving those who do not know You. [94]

"Do you suppose God will rescue those prisoners?" Eleazer asks.

"He most certainly will, but it may not be in the way that you are thinking. Just because God allows His children to die, does not mean that He does not deliver them. A believer who dies true to the Lord, dies victorious," I answer.

"I have so much to learn and so little time to do so," Eleazer answers.

"The most important thing to learn is that your Maker loves you and longs to be in relationship with you as He transforms you into His image," I respond.

"How does He transform us?"

"He uses anything and everything—suffering, victories, circumstances, nature, discipline, affirmation, failure. He causes all things to work together for good to those who love Him and to those who are called according to His purpose."[95]

The singing grows louder as others join in.

"The guards must all be outside or else those who guard us are all Christians," Laban states.

Eleazer says, "Peter, I do not understand all of this! How can you accept the fact that the God who can multiply bread, heal the sick, give sight to the blind, calm storms and drive out demons is doing nothing right now? Human beings are about to freeze to death, and He does nothing!"

"Eleazer, God is not behind this torture. Satan is. Evil men partner with Satan to carry out his wicked ways. There comes a time in your walk with God when you realize that you cannot always understand why God allows a particular thing to happen. It is during those times that you must stand in the midst of the injustice, pain and suffering and proclaim the truth that God is good and He cares."

"I do not believe that I could respond in such a way, for even now I find myself offended with God that He would do nothing to prevent the torture of His children," Eleazer confesses.

"God is doing something, my friend. We just can't always see heaven's side of the story. Right now, Jesus is covering them with His prayers. God has dispatched His ministering angels. And most importantly, He is with them, pouring His grace into them, which is sufficient to see them through. No one can snatch them from His hand, my friend.

"Eleazer, it is important that you realize that our enemy,

Satan, prowls about this earth like a roaring lion, seeking someone to devour. He wants you to be offended with God. He wants you to accuse Him as being heartless and cruel. Eleazer, you must resist him, and be firm in your faith, knowing that the same sufferings that those who are outside are experiencing are also happening to our brethren who are in the world.

"But that is not the end of the story, my friend. You see, Eleazer, after we have suffered for a little while, the God of all grace, who called us to His eternal glory in Christ, will Himself perfect, confirm, strengthen and establish us," I answer.[96]

"I find this way of life completely contrary to what I have known. I am accustomed to living in comfort and ease, not pain, sorrow and suffering," Eleazer responds.

"I understand, my friend. But, it is important to always look at the end of the story, for that is where we have the victory."

Paul shouts out, "Blessed be the God and Father of our Lord Jesus Christ! He is the Father of mercies and God of all comfort! He comforts us in our affliction so that we will be able to comfort those who are in any affliction with the same comfort with which we are comforted by God. For just as the sufferings of Christ are ours in abundance, so also our comfort is abundant through Christ!"[97]

"That is other side of the story, that is heaven's side of the story," I say.

Suddenly, there is a knock on our prison door, and a voice calls out, "The guards are returning."

Within minutes, the singing ends and all is quiet. Turning my attention back to my fellow prisoners, I quietly say, "If you are persecuted and reviled for the name of Christ, you are blessed because the Spirit of glory and of God rests upon you. By no means let any of you suffer as a murderer, thief, evildoer or a troublesome meddler, but if anyone suffers as a Christian, let him not feel ashamed, but in that name let him glorify God."[98]

"'Tis truth that you speak, Peter. I do not fully understand it, and I'm not in a place where I am walking in it, but I know your words to be truth," Eleazer states.

"As much as I would like to hear more about your time with Jesus, I can't help but think about those men and women out there freezing. Perhaps, we could spend some time praying for them?" Laban suggests.

"Excellent. Why don't you start, Laban?" I reply

Leaning against the post, I take great delight in hearing the prayers of my spiritual children. They are becoming more and more like Jesus.

We pray for hours, but because we cannot see outside, it is impossible to know for certain if morning has come or not.

At some point, I drift off to sleep. I wake when the door opens. Malchus quietly says, "It is finished, my friends; we lost only one."

"Only one died?" Eleazer asks.

I answer, "Malchus means only one denied the Lord."

"Is this true, Malchus?" Eleazer asks.

"It is true."

"What happened? How?" Eleazer asks.

"The ten emaciated prisoners were forced to sit on the cold ground. After a couple of hours, one of them, Archius by name, began to talk of denying Jesus. The others rallied around him, trying desperately to encourage him and warm his body, but sadly, he pushed them away. Just a short time later, he began shouting that Jesus was not the Son of God. He then ran from them to the large bonfire that the other guards sat around.

"I had assigned myself the task of standing beside my fellow Christians because I could not bring myself to enjoy the warmth of the fire while my brothers and sisters were in such agony.

"The guards celebrated, giving him warm clothing and hot food. Surprisingly, one of the guards, Barnabas by name, jumped up yelling, 'This is insane! Jesus is indeed the Son of God! I can no longer pretend that I do not see the truth! I want to know Him!'

"He then ripped off his clothes. The other guards were furious at what they viewed as betrayal. They cursed and mocked Barnabas as he ran to join the Christians. As he passed by me, I said, 'Today you will be with Jesus in paradise.'

"With tears streaming down his face, Barnabas took Archius's place among the believers whose tears for Archius's betrayal were now mixed with joy at Barnabas's conversion."

"And what of the ten? Are they all dead?" Eleazer asks.

"Their mortal bodies are dead, but their spirits live on! They now stand in the glorious presence of the Son of God where their nakedness has been covered with God's very own robe of righteousness and on their head is a glorious martyr's crown!" Malchus answers.

"What happened to Barnabas?" Eleazer asks.

"While I carried off the last body, the soldiers killed Barnabas."

"What?!" Eleazer exclaims.

"Barnabas exchanged this life for a martyr's crown, my friend," Malchus replies.

"I do not understand the ways of this King. He has the power to do miracles, but does nothing to help," Eleazer admits.

"God was with them and they sang their way into His arms," Malchus states.

"What will happen to Archius?" Eleazer asks.

"Archius awaits Nero's pardon. I will go to him at the

first opportunity that I might encourage him to not trade the temporal for the eternal, the fleeting comfort of this life for the eternal glory that can be his," Malchus states.

"I will pray for Archius to be restored to the Lord," I say feeling the agony of his denial having denied the Lord myself so many years ago.

"And so shall we," my fellow prisoners add.

"We shall remember you in our prayers as well," I add. "May God grant you success in reaching Archius."

The door closes, and my heart is heavy; it grieves me deeply to hear of anyone denying the Lord.

"Peter, the transformation that is taking place in my heart is real. I have never experienced the peace that I now have, and it is all because of the reality of Jesus in my life. I cannot say that I understand His ways, but strangely, I trust Him. I want to please Him. I want to give my life for Him," Laban states.

"You already have, my friend," I respond.

Eleazer says, "Tell us more, Peter, tell us more about the King."

"I shall, but first let us take the time to pray for Archius and Malchus."

My fellow prisoners cry out with great fervency and tender compassion. The transformation that is happening in them is beautiful to behold.

CHAPTER TWENTY

A fter feeding the four thousand, we sailed to the coasts of Magadan, which is on the western side of the sea. No sooner did we step foot on the beach than a group of Scribes and Pharisees approached Jesus but said nothing to Him, for they were far too busy arguing among themselves about the Master. Finally, one of them turned to Jesus and said, "If you are who you claim to be, then give us a sign from heaven."

In my lifetime, there have been several who have claimed to be the Messiah, and each one promised astonishing signs such as parting the Jordan river or making the city walls fall down with a word. But I have never seen Jesus do a single miracle for the purpose of proving who He is, and neither have I seen Him do so in order to provide food for curious appetites.

Knowing everything, even the motive of their hearts, Jesus sighed deeply and answered, "Why does this generation seek for a sign? Truly I say to you, no sign shall be given to this generation.

"When it is evening, you say, 'It will be fair weather

because the sky is red.' And in the morning you say, 'There will be a storm today because the sky is red and overcast.'

"You know how to discern the appearance of the sky, but you cannot discern the signs of the times! A wicked and adulterous generation is asking for a sign, and yet there are signs all around you!"

He stepped closer and continued, "You have broken your covenant with God. You pretend great love and zeal with your mouth, but your hearts are far from Him. You have other loves, other gods such as religious forms, ceremonies and traditions.

"An evil and adulterous generation seeks after a sign, but a sign will not be given it, except the sign of Jonah."

Having said this, He turned away. The Scribes and Pharisees stared after Him. It was obvious that they were highly insulted. Jesus climbed back into the boat, and not waiting for an invitation, we jumped in right behind Him.[99]

We set sail for Decapolis, the very place we had just left. Jesus was quiet the entire time. He stared out across the water obviously deep in thought or more likely, lost in prayer.

I could not help but think it ridiculous that the Pharisees and Scribes would ask Jesus for a sign. After all, they were aware of the miracles that Jesus had done, but they did not value His deeds of compassion. Instead, they despised the things that He did which brought relief to the suffering, such as healing the sick and bringing freedom to the oppressed.

Jesus refused to allow Himself to be manipulated.

Arriving at land, Andrew and I pulled the boat ashore. Having secured it, we followed Jesus along the shoreline. "Watch out," He said, "and beware of the leaven of the Pharisees, the Sadducees and Herod."

He then walked on. Bewildered, we stopped. "What is He saying?" I asked.

"I don't know," James responded.

I looked at the others; it was obvious that they did not understand either.

Beware of the leaven....

Suddenly, I understood. "We forgot to bring bread again, didn't we?" I asked.

Judas answered, "It wasn't my turn! It was John's."

Every eye looked at John. Judas remarked, "If you would stop hanging on the Master so much, maybe you'd be able to keep up with your responsibilities."

I intervened, "Jesus must have known that we forgot to bring bread."

John finally spoke up, "We do have one small loaf, but that will hardly feed thirteen hungry men."

"He is warning us," James replied.

"Against what?" Matthew asked.

"Against buying bread from the Pharisees, Scribes and Herod," I answered.

"What else could He mean?" James said.

"Come, let us all make a vow to never buy bread from them again," I suggested.

"And let us also vow to never eat with them or be friends with them," Judas added.

Kicking a stone, John mumbled, "If only I had remembered to bring the bread."

At this point, Jesus turned around. He looked really tired as He walked back to us. Placing His arm around John's shoulder, He asked, "Why are you discussing the fact that you have no bread? Don't you see? Don't you understand? Having eyes, do you not see? And having ears, do you not hear? Don't you remember when I broke the five loaves and fed five thousand?"

"I remember," I proudly answered.

"Do you also remember that there was food left over? Do you remember how many baskets full of broken pieces you picked up?"

"Twelve," several of us answered.

"And when I broke the seven loaves for the four thousand, how many large baskets were filled with the leftover pieces?"

"Seven," we answered.

"Then, how is it that you do not understand that I spoke to you not about *bread*, but that you should beware of the *leaven* of the Pharisees and Sadducees and Herod!"

The leaven? Of course! Leaven is a symbol of sin, of evil.

Revelation hit me like a fish swallowing the bait on a hook. With great excitement I shouted, "I got it! I understand! You are telling us to guard ourselves not from the yeast in bread, but from the teaching of the Pharisees, the Sadducees and Herod! You're telling us not to do the things that they have done, not to live our lives in the way that they live theirs!"

Like a teacher when his student grasps a new truth, Jesus responded with great joy. And pride filled my heart.

Jesus then said, "Except your righteousness exceeds that of the Scribes and Pharisees, you cannot enter into the Kingdom of heaven."[100]

As we walked along, I thought about the three groups of people that Jesus warned us of. From outward appearances, the three seemed to be nothing alike. The Pharisees were excessively zealous in their beliefs, the other two were extremely moderate. The Pharisees were hypocrites; they said one thing and did another. The Herodians and the Sadducees were consumed with material and temporal affairs.

It was true that the three were very different, but one thing that all three had in common was that they were very worldly minded. Because Jesus was unwilling to conform to their traditions, customs and man-made rules, they opposed Him. They were spiritually blind, not recognizing good when they encountered it, neither did they love or embrace it when they came to know it.

Their understanding of the Kingdom of God was that it was a temporary, earthly kingdom based on human power and greatness. Jesus demonstrated many signs and evidences of His infinite goodness and love, yet it was not enough for them. They continually demanded outward signs, external evidences, but inwardly they were ravenous wolves.[101]

No wonder Jesus is warning us about them.

Jesus led us northward along the banks of the Upper Jordan. We stopped in Bethsaida where some men brought a blind man to Jesus saying, "Rabbi, would You but touch the man? Would You open his eyes?"

Jesus looked closely at the blind man. Gently laying His hand on the man's shoulder, He said, "Come, let us go to a private place."

He led the man by the hand outside the village. Always curious, I followed. The Master spit on the man's eyes and then laid His hands on him.

"Do you see anything?" Jesus asked.

"I see men, but they look like trees walking about," the man answered.

Jesus laid His hands on the man's eyes again. "Now tell me what you see."

"I can see clearly now," he answered, trembling from head to toe. His now seeing eyes filled with tears.

Jesus responded, "Go home, My friend, but do not enter the village."

With a thankful heart the man hurried home.[102]

Leaving Galilee, we climbed into a boat and headed for Caesarea Phillippi. We passed by the plain where Jesus so recently fed the five thousand, and we then traveled on passing near Bethsaida. After two days, we arrived at our destination, camping just outside Caesarea Philippi, the capital of Phillip the Tetrarch.

Warming myself by the fire, I gazed at the surrounding country, which was beautifully situated near the mouth of the Jordan at the southern base of Mount Hermon. Before me were beautiful green hills, and in the background was the majestic Lebanon mountains.

Nearby, on the hillside, was said to be the birth place of Pan, the Greek god of nature. A temple had been erected in that place in his honor. Further up the hill was another temple. It was made of beautiful white marble, which Phillip had built as a place to worship Caesar, the Roman emperor and ruler of the world, who many considered a god.

This area was certainly beautiful, but it was mostly Gentile territory, which made it completely undesirable to the Jewish people.

In this remote, secluded place, surrounded by the gods of Greece, we set up camp. In this place, Jesus spent many nights in prayer while spending His days teaching us more about His Kingdom.

It was still early; the sun was just beginning to rise when I woke. Miriam slept soundly beside me. The diversity of sounds that a waking world makes has always intrigued me. I have always enjoyed the morning.

I watched as Jesus quietly made His way back to our campsite.

He has spent another night alone in prayer.

The others still slept. The morning sun was casting its golden light on the earth. The dew on the various patches of grass glistened like the sun shining on the sea.

The Master drew close; I stirred not. Stopping just on the edge of our campsite, He stood as a shepherd would, inspecting His flock, determining the state of its well-being.

Noticing that I was awake and watching Him, He smiled at me. I was suddenly flooded with the reality that this extraordinary Man deeply loved me and perfectly cared for me, a simple, uneducated fisherman! I could see, in His dark brown eyes, the great tenderness He felt for me, and my heart was moved beyond belief! He looked at me with such kindness that I would have climbed the highest mountain or swam the deepest sea if He would have asked me to at that moment.

Tears filled my eyes, which was very strange for me, a tough fisherman from Galilee.

How is it that Jesus feels such love for me? I know my many areas of weaknesses and so does He. He knows everything about me and still He loves me. How is it possible?

After so powerfully communicating the depths of His affection, Jesus turned His attention to the others. Standing over each one, He whispered a prayer.

I wonder just how many times He has prayed over us while we slept?

One by one, the others woke. Siloam, one of the women who had left all to follow Jesus, stepped out of a tent and greeted Jesus. Jesus' mother followed. Within minutes, the camp was busy with activity as each person fulfilled his or her responsibilities. Jesus rekindled the fire while Andrew picked figs from a nearby tree. Siloam and the two Mary's fashioned loaves of bread from a lump of dough. I hurried off to fill our water bags from the stream. When I returned, Jesus was holding up a basket and thanking God for our food.

He never fails to thank God.

After we had eaten, John pulled out his flute and began to play.

After a few moments, Jesus asked, "Who do the multitudes say that the Son of Man is?"

Judas answered, "Some say that You are John the Baptist."

"Who else do they say that I am?"

"Some are saying that You are Elijah," James stated.

"Who else?" Jesus asked.

"Others say that You are Jeremiah or one of the prophets," Andrew added.

Staring into the fire, Jesus asked, "But whom do *you* say that I am?"

Somewhere deep within I knew the answer, I knew the truth!

Jesus is the Messiah—the One we have been waiting for! He is the Messiah destined to rule and reign on the throne of David!

This revelation hit me like a bolt of lightening. I was terrified and thrilled at the same time.

With great enthusiasm, I exclaimed, "You are the Christ, the Son of the living God! You are indeed the Anointed One, the Messiah!"

John immediately stopped playing, and the women stopped their serving; even the birds grew silent.

Jesus placed His hand on my shoulder and responded, "Blessed are you, Simon, son of Jonas, because man has not revealed this to you, but this revelation has come from My Father who is in heaven."

Here we are in this Gentile land, and Jesus is speaking to me in Aramaic to me, a Jew! Why? For what purpose?

"I also tell you this: You are Peter, a man of rock. And on this rock, I will build My church, and the gates of Hades will not overcome it. I will give you the keys of the Kingdom of heaven. Whatever you prohibit on earth will be prohibited in heaven, and whatever you permit on earth will be permitted in heaven."

The greatest time in Israel's history was the days of king David. I have dreamed since a young boy of the day when another king would rise from David's lineage and make Israel great and powerful again. But, I never dreamed that I would rule with Him! There will be a throne, a government, a king again in Jerusalem, and I am to have charge over the keys!

The keeper of the keys is one of the most important roles a person can have whether that person be a servant, a high official or a priest. And I will be that person—imagine that!

Jesus continued, "Tell no one that I am the Messiah."[103]

How can something this exciting, this magnificent, be kept secret? Is it possible to hide the sun in the sky? Can an apple tree growing in the midst of a desert be hidden? How can one not see a majestic and lofty mountain? Oh, Jesus what You ask is not possible!

Jesus' mother handed Him a piece of pomegranate. As He bit into its flesh, dark red juice flowed down His arm, dropping onto the ground. I stared at the red dirt. Wiping the red liquid from His arm, Jesus said, "I must go to Jerusalem and suffer many things at the hands of the elders, the chief priests and the Scribes. They will kill Me, but I will be raised up on the third day."

What is He saying! This cannot be! This is impossible! All my life, I have been taught that the Messiah would be the most powerful conqueror in history. He is suppose to completely destroy our enemies, making Palestine the center of the world; the other nations would be subject to us. Peace and prosperity would fill the earth. But, what He says totally contradicts what all of Israel believes! I cannot bear the thought of what He is saying—it is absolutely impossible!

Jumping up, I grabbed His arm and pulled Him a short distance away. Planting my feet firmly, I rebuked Him saying, "God be merciful to You and forbid it! This shall never happen to You!"

Jesus laid His hand on my shoulder, looked directly into my eyes and said, "Get behind Me, Satan! You are a stumbling block to Me, for you are not setting your mind on God's interests but on man's!"

I shook under the weight of His words, which cut through me like a sword, leaving me powerless to say more.

Once I gathered my composure, I looked over the

Master's shoulder at the other apostles; it was obvious that they had heard the entire conversation. I turned and walked away.[104]

Jesus called after me, but I pretended not to hear. Once I was out of sight, I fell to my knees.

Will I ever learn?

I looked at the hillside. Glaring down at me was the temple of white marble built to honor Caesar. "Beautiful, isn't it?" A voice inside my head asked.

It is beautiful, but it is so empty.

I turn my back to the temple.

Who will I bow down to? Man or God? Truth or fiction? Comfort or suffering? Pride or humility?

I pick up a stick and throw it as far as I can.

Strange that in this place I would proclaim Jesus, a homeless Rabbi from Nazareth, to be the Son of the living God, the Messiah, and then only moments later dare to correct Him. Talk about going from one extreme to another.

I may not understand a lot, but I know that it would be foolish to allow my pride to keep me from Him.

Having licked my wounds, I sheepishly returned. And, consistent with His nature, Jesus warmly and happily received me just as if nothing had happened. But, I heard Judas and Thomas saying that maybe I was the traitor that Jesus spoke of. After telling them what they could do with their theory, I stormed off in search of better company.

From that night on, Jesus spoke often and in very plain words that He was going to Jerusalem and would suffer many things from the elders and Scribes and be killed and raised up on the third day. Even though He spoke plainly, none of us could understand because it was completely inconceivable.

We spent many days with Jesus in this secluded place. I treasured these times, except for the times when He spoke of the suffering that He would endure, which made no sense to me and troubled me greatly. It was beyond my understanding how He was going to establish His Kingdom and rule on the throne of David if He was going to be rejected by the Pharisees, Scribes and elders. No one could ever rise to a place of authority and certainly not to the throne in Jerusalem without the endorsement of these powerful men.

In spite of my confusion, I began to see Jesus in a new light. I could not explain it, but something was happening in my understanding and in my heart, something powerful and radical. I was beginning to deeply love this Rabbi of Israel who certainly, in my estimation, could and should be our next king.

The inevitable day came when Jesus led us into the neighboring villages. It was only a matter of hours before the crowds discovered His whereabouts and flocked to Him.

Gathering them like a hen gathers her chicks, Jesus said, "If anyone wishes to come after Me, let him deny himself and take up his cross and follow Me. For whoever wishes to save his life shall lose it, but whoever loses his life for My sake and the gospel's sake shall save it. For what does it profit a man if he gains the whole world and loses his own soul? For what shall a man give in exchange for his soul?

"Whoever is ashamed of Me and My words in this adulterous and sinful generation, the Son of Man will also be ashamed of him when He comes in the glory of His Father with the holy angels. If you are afraid to stand for truth in this hour, then you cannot expect a place of honor in the Kingdom of God.

"My friends, once a soul is lost, it is lost forever."

Forever is a long time.

Walking among the people, He said, "Truly I say to you, there are some of those who are standing here who shall not taste death until they see the Kingdom of God after it has come with power."

His words were weighty and filled great authority.

From that day forward, not only did He tell us that He was going to suffer, but He also spoke plainly of the sufferings that would come to those who followed Him. He promised His followers a garden but not a carefree garden. The garden He offered would be filled with weeds, thorns and pests and would require a lot of hard work.

The Master's words were shocking, for He said, "Not only shall I be crucified, but you too shall have a cross to bear."

This meant that those who obeyed His bidding would be regarded as criminals and punished accordingly. He did not offer us a carefree life—He offered glory but at a high price.[105]

Jesus never lured men into following Him, but He certainly invited all to follow. Neither did He promise an easy path. On the contrary, He taught us to deny ourselves, to say no to our own natural love for ease and comfort, to say no to things that were forbidden; He taught us to not even taste, touch or handle those things. We learned to say no to everything that was based on self-seeking and self-will. Over time, I learned that it was no longer I who lived but Christ who lived in me, for that is true freedom.[106]

I looked at the Master. He was resting underneath the branches of a fig tree. His eyes were closed. I sat down beside Him. Without even opening His eyes to see who had joined Him, He said, "Peter, it is possible to sacrifice eternity for a fleeting moment of pleasure, comfort and riches."

"How can I avoid such a painful fate, Jesus?"

"View things from an eternal perspective and not from a temporal one. Every detail of your life, everything that you do during your short lifetime has a direct effect in eternity. Seek to view things as God sees them, My friend."

"What You describe sounds impossible," I responded.

"With men this is impossible, but with God all things are possible."[107]

CHAPTER TWENTY-ONE

Eleazer interrupts, "Peter, I can't believe it! One minute you are proclaiming that Jesus is the Messiah, the Son of God, divine and all-knowing, and the next minute you are rebuking Him! What were you thinking?"

"Can you not put yourself in my place, you who are a fellow Jew? I had no idea the Messiah would be a suffering Messiah. It did not seem possible to me that the Messiah would subject Himself to the things Jesus spoke of, things such as shame, suffering and death. At the time, I only thought about the fact that I did not want Jesus to die. How did I know that His death would purchase and redeem mankind?

"That truth did not fit what I had been taught my whole life. My theology, as was yours, my brother, was that the Messiah would march into Jerusalem on a white horse with His powerful army and annihilate our enemies, driving them out of Israel. He would then lead us on to world power.

"All I could see was that if what Jesus was saying was

true then all that I had based my hopes and dreams on would come crashing down around my feet. What He told us in no way fit my belief system.

"After His resurrection, I came to understand why He died. I also came to understand that one of the reasons He died on a cross was to demonstrate to the world just how great His love really is. It took some time before I understood that the cross was beautiful and that it was the glory of God.

"When I rebuked the Lord and told Him that He could not die, I did not understand that He had left His throne in heaven in order to embrace a cross on earth. I did not know that He was the Passover Lamb, which would take away the sins of the world. And neither did I understand that Jesus had to bear the shame of the cross so that He could bear the burden of our sins.

"And so it was that I unknowingly joined Satan's team and basically told Jesus that it was okay to ignore God's plan and save Himself in order to secure His own comfort and pleasure. My friends, Satan's advice is always the same: forget about doing the right thing, forget God and please yourself; let self-interest be your god. Rightly, did the Lord rebuke me!"

"Where did Jesus die?" Eleazer asks.

"Eleazer, my fellow Jewish brother, you know yourself that it is written that a prophet cannot perish outside of Jerusalem. Jesus was not to die in an obscure place or in an obscure way. No, the Son of God must die in the most public place and in a judicial manner. He had to be lifted up so that all of Israel might look on the One they pierced, so that, by His stripes, we might be healed. Therefore, the Passover Lamb had to be sacrificed in Jerusalem where all legal sacrifices were offered."[108]

"Of course; I knew that," Eleazer replied, chuckling.

I believe that is the first time I have heard Eleazer laugh.

"Why did Jesus tell you beforehand that He was going to die?" Laban asks.

"He was preparing us for the dark hour that He knew was just around the corner, but we were oblivious to that reality."

Eleazer responds, "Years ago, I heard the rumors that a man named Jesus had been crucified because He claimed to be the Son of God. Now I know that it was so much more than a rumor and that Jesus was so much more than a prophet. He was truly the Son of God, and my people crucified Him!"

"It is as you say. Jesus was condemned by the rulers of Israel, but the people of Israel and also the Gentile rulers had a hand in His trial and subsequent death. But, really, we all nailed Him to the cross. It is because of our sins that the Son of God died," I answer.

"A crucified Messiah! Who would have ever thought? I am amazed that you believed it, Peter—it must have seemed to you to be a scandal and a contradiction!" Eleazer exclaims.

"Jesus was never so beautiful, so glorious, so powerful as He was hanging on that tree! On that hill outside the city gates, our Beloved Savior suffered for all mankind that we might live. He gave no thought to His personal desires, comfort or pleasure but completely gave Himself to His Father's will—all for the sake of love! Hanging there, He demonstrated how we are to live our lives. Oh, how beautiful and glorious He was and is and evermore will be!"

"I never knew—," Eleazer responds his words fading into the darkness.

I continue, "Not only did the news that Jesus would ultimately suffer and die shake the very foundations of all that we believed, but then He went on to inform us that we, too, would suffer. We were unable to even remotely conceive of that, so we chose to ignore it all!"

"Looking back over your life, Peter, His words have certainly been true, have they not?" Laban asks.

"Everything happened just as He said it would. Jesus knew the end from the beginning. He knew it all. It is easy to trust One who is as powerful as this."

CHAPTER TWENTY-TWO

It was an extremely hot summer day, so we were relieved when Jesus called James, John, and myself to His side saying, "Follow Me up the mountain."

Leaving the other apostles behind, we excitedly followed the Lord on the only road that led from Caesarea Philippi to mount Hermon. We first traveled through hills covered with vines and dotted with mulberry, apricot and fig trees. We then passed through cornfields where pear and fig trees grew along the outside perimeters. Then we began our ascent up the mountain path. The further we traveled, the sparser and smaller the shrubs became. As we continued, the path grew steeper, and the air grew cooler, which was a refreshing break from the summer heat.

Jesus was silent throughout our journey but not us. We talked about how exciting it was to be included in this adventure, and the more we talked, the prouder we grew for being singled out in such an obvious way.

With the setting of the sun and the appearance of the full moon, Jesus stopped, saying that we would camp for the night. We looked around for the best place to spread out our pallets, but Jesus immediately knelt on the ground, drawing His prayer shawl over His head.

He hasn't eaten all day.

The three of us decided to sit on a nearby rock. The air was quite cool, so we wrapped our cloaks around us.

I am really hungry. I wonder if He would mind if I ate? He probably wouldn't even notice.

Pulling a loaf of bread from the basket Miriam packed for us, I broke off a piece and then handed it to John and James. Jesus was lost in prayer. Once we ate, having nothing else to do, we decided to pray since that was what Jesus was doing. But, I quickly ran out of things to say, so I looked around at this huge mountain that divided Jewish and Gentile lands.

What a wonderful view! I can see for miles, and it is absolutely breathtaking!

Higher up, the mountain was covered in snow, which wonderfully reflected the light of the moon. To my delight, a herd of gazelle bounded out of the trees and leaped over the rocks and crevices with a beauty and grace beyond description. I watched until they disappeared out of sight.

Jesus certainly brought us to a beautiful place. I wonder why we came here.

Weary from the journey and from the lateness of the hour, I laid my head back and stared up at the glorious night sky. The stars were absolutely brilliant against the dark blue curtain. I soon fell asleep. How long I slept, I had no idea, but I woke with a start. Sitting straight up, I looked around. The entire mountain top was bathed in blinding, glorious light! I looked at Jesus, and my heart nearly stopped—such was the terror I felt! Kicking James and John, I woke them that they might confirm the awesome and terrible sight before my eyes.

They gasped as they gazed on Jesus who was still kneeling, but His uplifted face shone like the noonday sun!

Blinding light, brighter than the whitest white, came from within His entire being, flowing through His garments as though they did not exist. He was full of power and glory, wrapped in light as a garment!

Suddenly, out of nowhere, two men appeared beside Jesus. They, too, were cloaked in glorious splendor.

Straining to hear what they were saying, I leaned forward and nearly fell off the rock. Gathering my composure, I listened closely as the three of them discussed Jesus' death in Jerusalem.

When Jesus addressed the two men as Moses and Elijah, I did fall off the rock.

Moses? Elijah? It can't be! Moses and Elijah, here, now, with us? Oh, wait until the guys hear this!

Suddenly, from out of nowhere, a cloud of glorious light formed above us and then began descending upon us. Terrified, James, John and I scrambled to a nearby cleft in the rock where we hid ourselves.

A thunderous voice exploded from within the cloud. With my hands over my ears and my body trembling violently, I joined James and John on the ground, burying my face in the dirt. I was thoroughly and completely terrified as the thunderous voice said, "This is My beloved Son, with whom I am well-pleased, in whom I have chosen; listen to Him!"

Once my pounding, racing heart settled down, I dared to look up. To my relief, the cloud was gone and so were the heavenly visitors. Jesus alone was left.

"My friends, do not be afraid," Jesus called out to us.

Stumbling to my feet, I scrambled forward. Kneeling before Him, I said, "Lord, it is good for us to be here! If it pleases You, I will build three tabernacles—one for You, one for Moses and one for Elijah!"

Building tabernacles seemed like the only logical thing to do because that is exactly what our forefathers did in the wilderness when the presence and glory of God was among them. I could not help but notice the similarities.

In that day, Moses' face was radiant, and Jesus stands here with His face swallowed up in glorious light, still shining like the sun. A cloud covered Mount Sinai as God gave Moses the Law, and here we are on this mountain and a cloud just covered us and the voice of God thundered from heaven!

Is Jesus a type of Moses? Has He come to lead us out of Roman bondage and into the land of promise like Moses led our forefathers out of Egyptian bondage?

Trembling, I slowly and with great trepidation stood up. Fear still coursed through my veins, causing my legs to tremble before this One who only moments before shone like the noonday sun and caused the God of heaven to speak once again.

"Come, let us sleep until the break of day," Jesus casually said as though no great thing had just occurred.

Like men in a trance, we could not move but merely watched as Jesus spread our pallets on a nearby patch of thick mountain grass. Jesus sat on His pallet and called to us once more.

Moving ever so slowly towards Him, James whispered, "Do you think that cloud of glory will return? Do you think Elijah and Moses will show up while we are asleep?"

"I don't know, but if they do, I would rather be close by the Master's side than on my own," John answered as he quickened his pace.

Stretching out beneath the sky, the moon and stars did not seem as bright or as glorious as they seemed before.

After seeing what I have just seen, I don't imagine anything will ever look the same to me.

"Jesus?"

"Yes, John?"

"I have never known anyone like You! You are the kindest, most compassionate and gracious Man I have ever known. You are slow to anger and abounding in lovingkindness. You do not deal with people according to their sins and iniquities. Instead, You pardon us and heal our diseases. You rescue people from the pit and place a crown of life on their heads."[109]

"That is true, John," Jesus replied.

John sat up and said, "As far as the east is from the west, that is how far God has removed our transgressions from us. Just as a father has compassion on his children, so God has compassion on those who revere Him. He knows our frame. He understands how weak and needy we are, how much like sheep we are."[110]

"A Shepherd lays His life down for His sheep," He responded.

Looking at the great expanse above me, I added, "As high as the heavens are above the earth, that is how great Your lovingkindness is, Jesus. You are the light of the world!"[111]

Gazing at the heavens above, I exclaimed, "Bless the Lord, O my soul! God is very great! He is clothed with splendor and majesty. He is covered with light as with a cloak. He stretched out heaven like a tent curtain. He makes the clouds His chariot and walks upon the wings of the wind.

"He established the earth upon its foundations so that it will not totter forever and ever. The high mountains are for the wild goats; the cliffs are a refuge for the rock badgers. He made the moon for the seasons; the sun knows the place of its setting.

"Oh, Lord, how many are Your works! Let the glory of the Lord endure forever!"[112]

"Beautifully said," Jesus replied.

"King David said it first," James responded.

"He did indeed," Jesus answered.

John pulled out his flute and worshipped the God of

heaven. Jesus sang along; His countenance was filled with perfect peace.

I soon fell asleep.

With the rising of the sun, Jesus led us down the mountain. I followed in silence for a while, which was somewhat unusual, but I was so deeply impacted by what I had seen that I could not stop thinking about it.

I actually saw Moses and Elijah! I can't wait to tell the others!

I struggled to keep up with Jesus. He seemed to be in a hurry.

Moses and Elijah actually appeared and spoke. What was it that they said? Oh yeah, they talked to Jesus about His suffering and death.

Why all this talk of suffering? Moses and Elijah, two of the greatest heroes in Israel's history, didn't suffer. Moses died painlessly; his eyes were not dim nor was his strength diminished. As for Elijah, he didn't die at all but was taken up into heaven in a chariot of fire. Now that's the way to go![113]

After witnessing such an incredible manifestation of God's glory resting on and flowing through Jesus, I cannot understand how anyone would ever be powerful enough to persecute, much less kill, Him. Surely, I have misunderstood what He has said. There must be another explanation for all this talk of suffering and death.

James came alongside John and me, saying, "I can't wait to tell the others what has happened!"

"I know what you mean," I responded.

Jesus stopped abruptly and turned to face us saying, "My friends, tell the vision to no one until the Son of Man has risen from the dead."

"But, why Lord?" I asked quite perplexed.

"They are not prepared to hear it," He answered.

The three of us looked at each other and nodded even

though we did not understand what He meant by that.

Jesus resumed His fast-paced descent. I turned to James and John and asked, "What did He mean by the phrase, 'risen from the dead'? "

"I have no idea," John answered.

"Perhaps, He speaks of the time when all men will be resurrected" James responded.

"Or maybe, He speaks in figurative language. After all, He is an expert at that," I suggested.

"Perhaps," John replied.

We discussed this mystery for quite some time.

The Scribes say that Elijah must come before the Messiah. If this is true, and Jesus is the Messiah, then I wonder why Elijah didn't stay?

Baffled, I hurried down the path to Jesus and asked, "Master, why do the Scribes say that Elijah must come first?"

Jesus answered, "Elijah does first come and restores all things. And yet it is written that the Son of Man will suffer many things and be treated with contempt. But I say to you, that Elijah has indeed come, and they did not recognize him, but they mistreated him and did to him whatever they wished, just as it was written of him. If they treated the forerunner in such a manner, what will they do to the Messiah?"

He paused for a moment and then continued, "So also the Son of Man is going to suffer at their hands."[114]

CHAPTER TWENTY-THREE

Eleazer interrupts, "Peter, forgive me, but I do not understand. Would you explain to me who this Elijah was that Jesus said had already come?"

"Jesus was talking about John the Baptist who came to prepare the way for the Lord," I answer. "The three of us left that mountain more convinced than ever that Jesus was indeed sent from God. We did not understand exactly who He was or how His life would play out, but we realized that there was definitely more to this carpenter from Nazareth than we had understood. We were beginning to believe that He was the long awaited for King of Israel, the Messiah, but we did not understand all this talk of suffering and crosses and death.

"We could not tell anyone about the supernatural occurrence that we had witnessed on the mountain until after His resurrection. Had we told, it would have only fueled the fires of jealousy and ignited even greater controversies. I did not realize it then, but Jesus knew exactly what He was doing and where He was headed, which was a hilltop in Jerusalem, a platform for three crosses. His death did not come as a surprise to Jesus. Nothing happened that He was not aware of ahead of time."

Laban interjects, "Why do you suppose Elijah and Moses came to Him on that mountain?"

"Looking back, I suppose it was no different than in the garden of Gethsemane. Just before Jesus was arrested, He took the same three apostles with Him into the garden and told us to watch and pray. We prayed but soon fell asleep just as we did on that mountain.

"Without any mortal man to comfort Him, Jesus suffered alone, agonizing in prayer. His Father, in His great mercy, sent angels to strengthen Him. Perhaps, Moses and Elijah were sent by God in response to Jesus' prayer just as the angels were sent in response to His prayer in the garden of Gethsemane? I don't know for sure, but I have often wondered that.

"Likewise, we see God encouraging Jesus from heaven as He called Him His beloved Son. It was as if the Father was saying to Jesus, 'Son, the One I love, You are on the right track; you are right on course. You have not set Your affections on the things of this world, neither have You pursued Your own selfish desires, but You have set My will above Your own. The reason You live is to save others, not Yourself. I am well-pleased with You.'

"You may think that Jesus did not need encouragement, but He was fully God and fully man, and men need encouragement; men need assistance from heaven; men need loving assurance and affirmation. And so the God of heaven spoke, and also sent Elijah and Moses to His beloved Son.

"And, in a way that we cannot fully understand, Jesus learned obedience through the things He suffered, and the same is true for us, my dear friends."[115]

Laban asks, "Why did you want to build shelters there? For what purpose, Peter?"

"In my zeal and ignorance, I desired to stay there in that secluded place, away from the demands of the crowds, and be with the Lord, Moses and Elijah. I was hoping that if I built shelters for them then perhaps they would remain with us.

"It only seemed natural for me to desire such a wonderful thing. After all, why would anyone want to leave such an awesome experience? After all, God came down and touched earth! It seems to be the tendency of the human heart to desire to stay in those places where God meets with us, not realizing that there is so much more awaiting those who follow the Lord regardless of where He leads.

"I also knew that the prophecies told that Elijah would return before the Messiah in order to restore the Kingdom. So, when Elijah and Moses appeared, I was excited; this was a sign that the Kingdom was soon to be restored, which turned out to be true, but it certainly looked different from what anyone had ever imagined.

"When Jesus spoke of persecution, suffering and the cross, which He often did, I did not really hear Him because I was too busy dreaming of the crown I would someday wear."

"I am glad that Jesus was willing to suffer, for I would be hopelessly lost had He chosen any other path," Eleazer says.

"Brother, I am so happy to see the transformation that has taken place in your heart! There is no greater joy for me than this," I respond.

Without us hearing his approach, a guard places his key in the prison door. I hold my breath until Malchus walks in armed with food and water. We greet each other, and then I ask, as he quickly dispenses the life-giving bread and water, "Has the Lord made a way for you to see Archius?"

"He has indeed, but I am sad to report that Archius remains firm in his denial of the Lord."

My heart sinks, and I respond, "My fellow prisoners, it is vital that we maintain an intimate relationship with Jesus and cultivate a way of life that is fully surrendered."

Malchus adds, "Is your love for the Lord great enough to enable you to walk on water? Or, at the first sign of trouble, do you retreat to the safety of your little boat, which is shaky at best?"

I respond, "Suffering is our best friend right now, for it has the capacity to produce in us deep faith if we will only allow it to. It is important for us to know that Jesus is our only true security and our only true hope."

Eleazer says, "Malchus, Peter, pray for us that we might remain true to the end just like Justus did."

"I have been and will continue to do so," I respond.

"As have I," Malchus adds. "I will continue to pray that you all will be strengthened with power through the Holy Spirit in your inner man. I pray that Christ will dwell in your hearts through faith. That you would be rooted and grounded in love and able to comprehend with all the saints what is the breadth and length and height and depth of God's love.

"Oh, that you would know the love of Christ which surpasses knowledge! I pray that you would be filled up to all the fullness of God! For He is able to do exceedingly abundantly beyond all that we ask or think, according to the power that works within us."[116]

"I must admit that I am afraid that my love will not be strong enough to endure persecutions for the sake of Jesus," Eleazer confesses.

"Your hope is never in yourself, my friend. Your hope is in the person of Jesus Christ who is able to complete that which He began. Your hope is in the fact that His love is greater than your weakness," Malchus answers.

"But it wasn't enough for Archius," Eleazer responds.

"It was. The problem was that Archius chose not to receive it. He chose to save Himself rather than allow the Lord to save Him. And, if you should face death on account of the Lord, you, too, will have the same choice. Will you save yourself or will you allow the Lord to save you either through a miraculous deliverance or your physical death which would result in glorious life eternal," Malchus answers.

"I see your point," Eleazer states.

"Peter," Malchus says, "I have news for you. The Lord made a way for me to see your wife just this morning. She continues to actively share the gospel with the women in her cell. None of them have surrendered their lives to the King, but she is not discouraged. She continues to pray and speak truth; it is only a matter of time before they accept His invitation to become part of His family. She sends her greetings and her love to you. She reports that she is well and inquired of your well-being."

Tears of joy fill my eyes. "Oh, this is indeed food for my heart! I praise God for His infinite lovingkindness! Should you see her again, my friend and brother, would you tell her that I constantly pray for her and love her dearly?"

"I would be glad to."

"Malchus, do you have any news of Paul?" I ask.

"Paul is well. He continues to preach the good news to everyone who will listen. I gave him your message and he was ever so grateful.

"Peter, throughout this prison, both men and women, guards and prisoners are boldly proclaiming the good news. Nero thinks that he is wiping out Christianity by arresting and executing Christians, but he is merely fueling the fire," Malchus answers.

Eleazer speaks up, "I would be thrilled to be able to tell at least one person about Jesus, but I do not suppose that will ever happen."

"I have seen God do greater things than what you desire, my friend and brother. One never knows what God will do. It never hurts to ask for what you want," Malchus responds.

Without hesitation, Eleazer responds, "I will do exactly that."

"And we will join you in asking," I say.

Before Malchus leaves, he prays for each one of us, and then disappears through the door that separates us from the world.

"Peter," Laban says.

"Yes?"

"I need to love Him more," Laban states.

"And so you shall," I respond.

CHAPTER TWENTY-FOUR

A s the four of us descended the mountain, from our vantage point, we could clearly see the valley below. A great crowd was gathered there.

It is strange to see a crowd gathered without Jesus in the middle of it. I wonder what's going on.

As we drew near, I could see the other apostles in the very center of the crowd. A group of Scribes stood around them like a pack of wolves surrounding its prey. It was obvious that they were in the midst of a heated argument. The people were so caught up in the debate that they did not notice Jesus approaching until He was in their midst.

A young boy shouted out, "The Master has come!"

The people seemed quite surprised and even shocked to see Jesus.

Perhaps, they feared that He would not return just as the Israelites became fearful that Moses would not return from Mount Sinai.

"At least they haven't built a golden calf."

"What did you say?" James asked.

"Oh, nothing. I was just thinking out loud," I answered.

The people quickly surrounded Him.

Positioning Himself directly in front of the Scribes, Jesus asked, "What are you discussing with them?"

Before they could respond, a very exhausted looking man stepped forward. His clothes were in disarray, and his hair was unkempt. He immediately fell on his knees before Jesus. Looking up he said, "Lord, have mercy on my son, for he is my only son. Behold, a spirit seizes him, and he suddenly screams, and it throws him into a convulsion; his mouth foams. The evil spirit mauls him and scarcely ever leaves him. I begged your disciples to cast it out, but they could not."

Jesus cried out in a loud voice, "O unbelieving and perverted generation, how long shall I be with you? How long shall I put up with you?"

He then turned to the desperate father still kneeling before Him and quietly said, "Bring your son to Me."

As the father scrambled to his feet, Jesus instructed the twelve of us to follow Him and commanded the crowd to remain. We went a short distance away where it was a little more private.

In a very short time, the father returned with his young son in tow. When the two were close, the demon dashed the boy to the ground and threw him into a convulsion. Jesus quickly went to the boy's side and asked his father, "How long has this been happening to him?"

"From childhood. It has often thrown him into the fire and into the water. It clearly wants to destroy him. If You can do anything, take pity on us and help us!"

"If I can?" Jesus responded looking deep into the man's eyes.

Laying His hand on the father's shoulder, Jesus said, "All things are possible to *him* who believes."

In heart-wrenching agony, the father desperately clutched Jesus' robe and cried out, "I do believe but help my unbelief!"

As the curious multitude was approaching, Jesus calmly rebuked the unclean spirit saying, "You deaf and dumb spirit, I command you, come out of him and do not enter him again."

The demon cried out, and for the last time, threw the boy into terrible convulsions, leaving him in a lifeless heap. The crowd rushed around the boy crying out, "The boy is dead! You have surely killed him!"

Shaking His head, Jesus took the boy by the hand and raised him up. The boy stood to his feet and was perfectly normal and completely healed! Jesus gave him back to his father.

The multitude was absolutely amazed. Shouts of praise and adoration filled the air as the people celebrated life and freedom and deliverance!

Jesus quickly left. We followed Him to the house where we would spend the night. After eating, we climbed the stairs to the roof. As we stretched out on our pallets under the great expanse of heaven, Matthew asked, "Teacher, why could we not cast that demon out?"

"You were unable to deliver the boy because of the littleness of your faith. Truly I say to you, if you have faith as a mustard seed," He said pointing to the nearby mountains, "You shall say to this mountain, 'Move from here to there,' and it shall move; and nothing shall be impossible to you."

A mustard seed is the smallest of seeds. Is He saying that it doesn't take much faith to do great things? Then why could they not cast that demon out?

Without my asking, Jesus answered, "That kind of evil spirit does not go out except by prayer and fasting."[117]

Pondering His words, I soon fell asleep and dreamed of thrones and war and power and wealth.

The following day, Jesus led us through the back streets

of Galilee in an effort to keep His whereabouts as hidden as possible.

Jesus is leaving the safety of the north country and heading towards Jerusalem, which is a very dangerous place for Him. Why does He risk His life by going there?

We stopped to set up camp for the night. John and I gathered fire wood and dried dung while the women busied themselves with the food preparations. With everything ready, we sat around the fire eating olives, raisins, goat cheese and bread.

Jesus said, "Let these words sink into your hearts, hear what I am saying, for the Son of Man is going to be delivered into the hands of men. They will kill Him, but He will be raised on the third day."

Kill Him? Raised on the third day? Whatever could this mean?

I turned to the other disciples and could tell by their expressions that they did not understand either.

How could anyone have the power to kill Him when He just demonstrated such absolute authority over an evil spirit that could not be cast out by any other? And what about the awesome supernatural display on the mountain?

He has demonstrated supernatural power and governmental authority so many times that I have lost count. And what about His destiny? If He is the Messiah, how can mere men have power over Him?

My heart was filled with sorrow, and my mind was confused, but I dared not ask any further questions. I much too afraid to hear more, so Miriam and I retired for the night.[118]

Stretched out under the night sky, I whispered, "Miriam, what do you think of all this talk about suffering and death?"

"I think that Jesus is trying to prepare us for some very painful events."

"You don't believe that He is going to die, do you?"

Without waiting for her response, I continued, "He can't die—He's the Messiah!"

"I do not know what manner of words Jesus speaks concerning suffering and death, but I do know that He is the greatest Man I have ever known. And I know that He certainly loves us. And I know that whatever happens, whether it be difficulties or blessings, it will be perfect and right and good. Jesus can do nothing but that, for He always puts Himself in the role of servant. Other than that, I do not know anything," she answers.

"Why does it have to be so complicated, Miriam? Why can't Jesus just be like the other rabbis?"

"You don't mean that. You don't really want Him to be like all the rest. Jesus is so much more than a rabbi, Peter. He is unlike anyone we have ever met—He is the Messiah, the Son of God who will one day rule and reign in Jerusalem! He is good and kind and perfectly selfless. He heals the sick and delivers the oppressed. He loves the poor and cares for the widow and orphan. He hates sin yet embraces the sinner. No, you do not want Jesus to be like all the others."

"Once more you speak truth," I said kissing Miriam good-night.

The following morning, we traveled through Galilee towards Capernaum, always taking the hidden routes. He spent most of His time speaking of His coming suffering, but we were much too busy dreaming of our own kingdoms to hear what He was really saying.

With each passing day, we came to believe that the long awaited for Kingdom was just on the horizon. It became quite clear to me and the other disciples that we had been chosen to rule and reign with Jesus in His Kingdom. What a glorious future we had! I could hardly sleep at night for thinking of the grand position that awaited me as the keeper of the keys.

We were nearly at Capernaum when the twelve of us got into a discussion about our roles in the coming Kingdom. The crowd surrounded Jesus to the point that we lost sight of Him. Andrew was the first to speak, "We shall all be great when the Kingdom comes!"

Thomas asked, "Shall we all be equal or shall one be higher than another in this Kingdom?"

"Peter, James and John will surely be higher than us. After all, they alone were chosen to ascend the mountain with the Lord," Judas replied.

"Surely that is not the way it will be," Bartholomew joined in.

"The Lord has chosen James, John and myself to be the closest to His side on several occasions," I responded, looking to be sure Jesus was not close enough to hear.

"That is true. And, we have been brought into His strictest, most intimate confidences," James added.

"He does seem to prefer us over the rest of you," John said.

"It may be that way now, but things can certainly change," Matthew replied.

"I think the one entrusted with the money will ultimately be the greatest," Judas stated.

"I think that the one who is the most gifted will be the greatest," Phillip added.

"The smartest will surely be the greatest," Thomas said.

"None of you know what you're talking about!" Judas exclaimed, shoving Thomas.

At this point, we got into a heated argument. Coming to no conclusion as to who would be the greatest, we separated quite offended with each other. I hurried to the Master's side. With Capernaum in sight, Miriam and I decided to walk along the sea while the others continued on to my house. The sun was low in the sky, and the fishermen were busy preparing for another night of fishing.

"It is good to be home, is it not?" Miriam asked.

"It is."

"Peter, do you miss the sea? Do you miss your fishing business?"

Thinking back, I responded, "No, Miriam, I do not. I may not understand everything that Jesus says; as a matter of fact, I think that there is more that I don't understand than I do." I looked across the beautiful sea and continued, "But regardless, I find life with Jesus much more rewarding than life on the sea. It is certainly filled with more surprises and more adventures than I could have ever had on the sea that I love so much."

The sea breeze blew a stray strand of Miriam's long black hair across her beautiful face. Tucking it back under her head covering, I asked, "What about you? Your life has been turned upside down because of the Master. You no longer have a normal life, whatever that is. Instead, you follow Him across this land and sleep on the ground and in barns and on roofs. At other times, you are left behind while your husband follows this Rabbi throughout Israel. This is certainly not the life I pictured for you when we were betrothed."

"I would not trade life with Jesus for all of king Solomon's wealth or comfort because I have found a richness that I never knew existed and I found it in a Man who has the heart of a King. And," she says placing her arm around the small of my back, "I have also gained a husband whose heart is becoming more like that of his Teacher."

"Do you think so, Miriam? I often wonder, for I look at Jesus and see His perfect character and relentless love and then turn my eyes to myself and see a wretched man with a divided heart.

"Every single day, I wonder how I will become even

remotely close to the goodness I see in Jesus. The main reason for being a disciple is to become like your Teacher. Anything less than that is not good enough. And I don't want to fail, Miriam."

"I struggle with the same fears, my husband, but I have come to the conclusion that I will never be perfect. All I can do is follow Him everyday to the best of my ability. My desire is to get as close as He will allow me to be, and so far, He has never turned me away or told me to withdraw or refused my pursuit. Instead, He continually draws me close and showers me with words of comfort and encouragement. He consistently reminds me that it is the power of His love and His strength and His grace that enables me to live a life of holiness.

"Simon, I cannot imagine Jesus ever turning anyone away, regardless of how sinful, how weak, how broken they might be," Miriam replied.

"I would agree; I have never seen Him refuse anyone who sought to follow Him," I responded.

"Peter, there must be a way to follow Him without failing Him? There must be a way to be free from the burden of our sins and human weaknesses. I know that it is impossible for the blood of bulls and goats to take away sins, but I do not know of anything that can.[119] If only there was some way to permanently do away with our sins and transform us into the nature and character of the Master, then we would be free. Oh, how priceless a gift like that would be!"

"Such a life-changing gift would have to be completely free; otherwise, humans would take credit for it. Such is human nature," I added.

"A perfect gift like this would have to come from above," she replied.[120]

"You are a wise woman with a lovely heart, oh wife of mine!" I said as I drew her close. We stopped on an overlook and watched the waves crash against the rocks until the setting of the sun.

Hand in hand, we headed home. Along the way, we came face to face with two men who collect the temple taxes. The eldest stopped me and asked, "Does your Teacher not pay the two-drachma tax?"

Swallowing quickly I answered, "Of course He pays it."

With a nod, they stepped aside, following us back to my house. Hurrying inside, before I could ask the question, Jesus looked up and said, "What do you think, Simon? From whom do the kings of the earth collect customs or poll-tax, from their sons or from strangers?"

"Of course they collect it from strangers," I answered.

"Consequently, the sons are exempt, for the royal family does not tax itself. If this is true, and it is, then why should I be taxed for the upkeep on My own Father's house?"

I stood before Him speechless, not quite sure what He meant.

Jesus looked at the two tax collectors who stood like greedy wolves in my doorway and continued, "They will not understand. Therefore, lest we give them reason to be offended, go to the sea and throw in a hook. The first fish that you catch, open its mouth, and you will find a coin. Take that and give it to them for you and for Me."

I turned, not exactly thrilled about my mission. The two men looked down their noses at me.

"For two cents, I would knock that smug look right off your face," I said under my breath.

Grabbing a hook and line, I hurried back to the sea; the two men followed closely behind.

I cannot believe Jesus asked me to do this! I am a professional fisherman, and everyone knows that professional fishermen don't fish with a hook and a line, they fish with a net from a boat! And they don't fish in the daytime, they fish at night when the fish can't see them.

To think that I have to go down to the sea where everyone knows me and fish with a hook and line is humiliating!

I was tempted to turn around and forget the whole thing, but looking over my shoulder at my two shadows, the tax collectors, I knew that I had no choice but to obey.

With the sea in sight, I kicked a stone saying to myself, "Why didn't Jesus just pull the coin out of a loaf of bread or something? Why this way? Why me? Why not Matthew? After all, he was a tax collector. He should have to be on this end of the tax collecting routine. He could gain quite a bit from having to do this, and no one would laugh at him for fishing with a hook from the shore either.

"I may as well get this over with since I don't have a choice," I muttered.

"Did you say something?" one of the tax collectors asked.

"Not anything important," I answered.[121]

CHAPTER TWENTY-FIVE

L aban says, "Pardon me, Peter, but I am not familiar with this tax that you speak of."

"The Law of Moses states that every man above twenty years of age must pay the sum of half a shekel as an atonement for his soul. This tax helps with the expenses connected with the public sacrifices, those which were offered for the sins of the whole congregation of Israel. Jesus, as a Jew, was under obligation to obey this Law just as all Jews," I answer.

Eleazer interjects, "The temple tax was meant to atone for one's life, and Jesus, being perfect, had no sins to atone for; therefore, there was no need for Him to pay that tax."

I respond, "That is true. I believe that Jesus paid the tax in order to, in every way, relate to sinners. Another reason that I believe He paid the tax was to keep an open door between Himself and the people. Refusing to pay such an important tax would only create a division between Him and the people, thus further alienating Him.

"It is important for us to never decline our duty for fear of giving offense, and equally important, we must

217

Rhonda Calhoun

sometimes deny ourselves those things which are perfectly legitimate rather than give offense.

"It was humbling for Jesus to pay this tax in the same way it would be humiliating for a king's son to pay a tax for the support of his father's palace. But, this was nothing new for Jesus, for, in the same manner, He left His position of royalty that He might become a man, a peasant, which was a voluntary act of humbling Himself.[122]

"Jesus could have refused to pay the tax, and He would have been perfectly correct to do so due to who He is. If He had been like us, proud, ambitious and striving for positions and titles, He would have stated who He was and refused to pay the tax. In like manner, He could have done the same thing and refused to embrace the cross. But, thankfully, in both cases, He did not do so."

"He is amazing, is He not?" Eleazer reflects.

"He is indeed," I respond.

Laban joins in, "Peter, like you, I was a professional fisherman, but that was before I lost my temper and killed a man. If Jesus had asked me to fish with a hook and line from the shore, I would have been so ashamed."

"My dear friends, I would be lying if I said it didn't bother me. Jesus knew exactly what He was doing. I was way too proud, and Jesus knew that. Walking down the roads of my hometown with a rod in my hand was bringing to the surface the dark, ugly pride in my heart.

"By the time I reached the sea, my head was hanging lower than the evening sun. My old fishing friends whispered and laughed as I walked past. As soon as I dropped my hook in the water, the laughter escalated. I could hear them mocking me for leaving in order to follow Jesus. I grew angrier by the minute. I was just getting ready to tell them off when I felt a tug on my line. I pulled in a very small fish, which caused my former friends to laugh even harder. But, when I reached into its mouth

218

and pulled out that coin, they stopped laughing.

"Several young boys ran over to me; their eyes were larger than the coin I held in my hand. Their questions came faster than I could answer. "Where did that come from? How did you do that? Are there any more fish in there like that one? Can you teach me how to fish like that?"

With great delight, I told them about Jesus and His miracle-working power.

With my head held high, I walked past my old friends. I was feeling quite proud of myself, too proud actually, which, like I said, was one of my weaknesses. I was a young man who was way too proud and way too self-focused. I believed that my strength lay in my own abilities, not in the Lord's ability to keep me. I was confident in me, not in the Lord. Thankfully, the Lord loved me too much to leave me in that pitiful, dangerous condition. But, that is a story for another day," I answer.

"Then tell us what happened next," Josiah says.

"After handing over the coin to the tax collectors, I returned to my home with my fish in hand."

CHAPTER TWENTY-SIX

Throwing open the front door to my house with a shout, I waved the miraculous fish in the air. Jesus and the other apostles reclined around the table waiting for supper. Throwing that little fish on the table, I exclaimed, "You should have seen the faces of those two tax collectors and my old fishing friends when I opened that fish's mouth and pulled out that coin! I thought their eyes were going to pop out of their heads! It's amazing how something as insignificant as this tiny fish can shut the mouths of scoffers."

As they passed around the fish for inspection, Miriam greeted me, gently scolding me for getting the floor muddy. Steering me to the bench, she washed my feet as I shared the events of the past hour in great detail, relishing each moment. Mary brought out a fresh bowl of water for me to wash my hands. I then joined the others around the table.

The women filled the table with delicious food, and we ate until we could eat no more, laughing and sharing stories all the while.

Jesus leaned forward surveying His little group of very

zealous, ambitious apostles and asked, "So, what were you discussing on the road?"

Looking at John, I held my peace; I was not about to admit that we had been arguing over who would be the greatest in His Kingdom. When no one answered, Jesus rose from the table and invited us to follow Him. He led us outside and then around the side of the house to the steps that led to the rooftop. "Shall we?" He said, motioning for us to go up.

Pushing past John, I quickly made my way up the steps. Standing on the roof, I looked down as the others pushed and shoved each other; Jesus waited patiently bringing up the rear. I waited to see where He was going to place His pallet before unrolling mine. Of course, I placed mine close by His side. We sat around the Master waiting to hear what He had to say.

From His expression, this must be very serious.

He began by simply looking at each one of us, which caused us all, one by one, to lower our heads. It felt as though He peered into the depths of my heart, which I later came to know was exactly what He was doing.

Jesus finally spoke, saying, "If anyone wants to be first, he must put himself last of all and be a servant of all."

Without us telling Him, He knows what we were talking about on the road.

"If you desire to be great, then you must be last; you must become a servant not a master. Ambition is not, in and of itself, bad, My friends. Be ambitious, but be ambitious to serve others out of a heart of love. Be ambitious to do things for others rather than have others do things for you. Be ambitious in esteeming your brother as greater than yourself."[123]

At this point, Miriam joined us followed by a group of our neighbors and their children. As they were gathering around the Master, I asked, "Who then is greatest in the

Kingdom of heaven?"

Jesus called the youngest of the children to Him. The toddler ran to Him squealing with delight. Jesus laughed and scooped the lad up in His welcoming arms.

It was remarkable how trusting this child was of Jesus. He only just met Him, and yet he was snuggled against His chest, simply receiving His love.

Rubbing the little one's back, Jesus said, "Whoever gives you a cup of water to drink because you are My follower, truly I say to you, he shall not lose his reward. Any help given, any kindness shown to My children shall never be forgotten and will most certainly be rewarded."

Setting the toddler on His knee, Jesus continued, "Truly I say to you, unless you become like children, you shall not enter the Kingdom of heaven."

I looked closely at the little boy now snuggled in the crook of His arm.

This little guy's motives are pure. He has no concept of self-promotion, striving for status or social position, which are the result of pride and ambition.

He has nothing to offer those in his life except his love, but he requires a lot of care because of his inability to meet his own needs. He is innocent of any ulterior motives or striving to be noticed by man; he simply enjoys being in the arms of the Master, receiving His love. Is this what Jesus means by saying that we must become like little children?

Jesus continued, "You desire to know who is the greatest in the Kingdom of heaven? Truly I say to you, whoever humbles himself as this child, he is the greatest in the Kingdom of heaven. And whoever receives in My name those who are considered the least, he receives Me. But, whoever causes one of these little ones who believe in Me to stumble, it is better for him that a heavy millstone be hung around his neck and that he be drowned in the depths of the sea."

Children have no position, privileges or status apart from the love of their parents and family, and yet Jesus certainly highly esteems them, which is true to His character and nature.

"Woe to the world because of its stumbling blocks!" Jesus announced. "It is inevitable that occasions of stumbling and offense will come; but woe to that man through whom the stumbling block comes!

"What then is the alternative? I say to you that if a situation arises where there is the potential for causing someone to stumble, then do whatever you have to do to protect that person. Put the condition of their soul over your ministry, your personal comfort and your selfish desires.

"If your hand or your foot causes you to stumble, then cut it off and throw it from you; it is better for you to enter eternity crippled or lame than having two hands or two feet to be cast into the eternal fire. And if your eye causes you to stumble, pluck it out and throw it from you. Be aggressive in your pursuit of this; do whatever you must do. I say to you that it is better for you to enter eternity with one eye than having two eyes to be cast into Gehenna, which is the darkest and most terrible of places."

He speaks of Gehenna, which is a deep valley just five minutes outside the southern gate in Jerusalem. This is the same place king Ahaz, many years ago, instituted fire worship and sacrificed children to the god Molech. Years later, king Josiah declared it to be unclean. Since that day, it has been used as a place to dump and burn the garbage from Jerusalem. It is a foul place, a place where maggots feed on the rotting garbage and human excrement. It is also the place where the Romans throw the crucified bodies. The fire smolders constantly, never going out. The ascending smoke smells disgusting and is enough to make a grown man sick. Of all places on the earth, surely Gehenna is the most despicable and despised. I don't even want to imagine what it would be like to be cast into that awful, disgusting place!

I squirmed uncomfortably; I could feel conviction stirring in my heart. I was wrong in striving to be seen as important so that others would serve me. Selfish ambition, pride and jealousy have a way of consuming one's heart like a sly fox sneaks up on and consumes the weak, sick and young among the flock.

Jesus continued, "For everyone will be salted with fire. Salt is good; but if the salt becomes unsalty, with what will you make it salty again? Have salt in yourselves, and be at peace with one another."

Every Jewish sacrifice must first be salted before it is placed on the altar where it is consumed. I understand that salt represents the incorruptible and that fire purifies and consumes the sacrifice. But what exactly is He saying?[124]

"See that you do not despise but rather embrace those in My Kingdom that this child represents—those of simple, humble faith; those who are completely and desperately dependent upon God in every way; those who are ordinary, poor and have no influence, no wealth and no power. As you embrace them, you embrace Me. Do not treat them as if they have no value, neither make fun of their behavior. You must not disdain them, neither treat them harshly or in a heartless manner lest you cause them to sin. For I say to you, that their angels in heaven continually behold the face of My Father."

At this point, the toddler reached up and patted Jesus' face. Jesus gave the lad His full attention. The boy threw his pudgy arms around Jesus' neck and hugged Him tightly.

Looking back on this, I find myself amazed that the beloved Son of God, the Creator of the universe, sat before me thoroughly enjoying that toddler's simple yet enthusiastic display of affection. At that moment in time, that small, insignificant little boy held the Creator's undivided attention and experienced His perfect affection. What kind of God loves like this? I know of no other. God is alone in His deity. There is no other god before Him!

With the child's arms still locked around His neck, Jesus said, "The Son of Man has come to save that which was lost.

"The Son of Man, who beheld the Father's face at all times, took no thought of His rights and privileges. Instead, He humbled Himself and became a babe among men in order to demonstrate the magnitude and power of His infinite, unconditional love. And it is through this love that His children will find salvation."

The little boy climbed down and ran toward the edge of the roof. Jesus immediately ran after him, catching him before he was even close to danger. Stroking the little boy's curly, black hair, Jesus asked, "What do you think? If a man has a hundred sheep, and one of them wanders off, does that man not leave the ninety-nine sheep that are safe in the pen and go in search of the one that is in danger?"

The men loudly responded that they would most certainly go after the lost one.

Jesus continued, "And if it turns out that he finds it, truly I say to you, he will rejoice over it more than over the ninety-nine which have not gone astray."

The toddler now tried to climbed onto His chest and shoulders as though He were a tree. "It is not the will of your Father who is in heaven that one of these little ones perish," Jesus said as He rescued the little one from toppling over.

Chuckling, He said, "Truly I say to you, unless you change and become like children you shall not enter the Kingdom of heaven."

This completely dependent, totally innocent and constantly in need of rescuing is what I am to be like? I have diligently worked for years to become independent and "grown-up," and now He tells us that we are to be like little children?

Jesus sat the little boy down; he happily ran back to his mother, clapping his hands the entire way.

Jesus continued, "If your brother sins, go and lovingly confront him in private; if he listens to you, you have won your brother. If he does not listen to you, take one or two more with you to be a witness and to reason the case further with him. If he refuses to listen to them, tell it to the body of believers; and if he refuses to listen even to the church, then treat him in the same manner as you have treated the Gentiles and tax-collectors."

Treat him like a tax gatherer, like a Gentile! Let the unrepentant sinner be excluded from religious and social fellowship. To do so would be so insulting to a fellow Jew!

"Let the law of love be the basis for your discipline, for this man is your brother, and you have a responsibility to care for his soul. Therefore, there are times when it is in his best interest for you to break off your friendship with him, though you must by no means seek revenge. It is because of your love for him that you are to take such drastic measures, in order to save his soul.

"Truly I say to you, whatever you shall bind on earth shall be bound in heaven; and whatever you loose on earth shall be loosed in heaven.

"Again I say to you, that if two of you agree on earth about anything, that they may ask, it shall be done for them by My Father who is in heaven. For where two or three have gathered together in My name, there I am in the midst of them."

With the setting of the sun, Jesus ended His message. My neighbors stood expressing their wonder and awe at the words of Jesus and the manner in which He spoke. They repeatedly thanked Him. The toddler escaped from his mother's arms and ran straight to Jesus who once more scooped him up. The little guy quite aggressively patted His cheeks and then gave a good hard tug on His beard, which caused both to laugh.

Children seem to be drawn to Jesus, and He certainly is drawn to them.

With a final hug, Jesus returned the little one to his mother. As Jesus was bidding them good-night, I stretched out on a pallet and watched.

Jesus, who is the greatest Rabbi I have ever known, is also the humblest Rabbi I have ever known or heard of. His humility is not based on the fact that He thinks little of Himself, but it is based on the fact that He does not think of Himself at all. His heart is consumed by what His Father desires and for what is best for mankind. He neither desires nor receives nor seeks honor from men, but seeks only the honor that comes from God. His soul is completely and perfectly satisfied to live for God and for the benefit of others, for He came to serve and not to be served. What an amazing Man He is in every way!

Once everyone was gone, Jesus unrolled His pallet and joined the twelve of us. He said nothing, but merely stretched out under the beautiful sky. Even though the sun had barely set, the evening star was already shining brightly.

I suppose this star is the greatest star in all the heavens.

"What does it mean to be great?" Jesus asked.

"I suppose it means that you shine more than all others, that you are more visible than all others, that you are more desired than all others," I answered.

"Is it worth the price that you must pay to attain such a temporal place of greatness?" He asked.

I dared not answer, for I was not sure what He meant.

Judas replied, "Sometimes it is worth it."

"Is it really?" Jesus asked looking right at him.

Judas returned His gaze for only a moment and then looked away.

I thought of the argument the twelve of us had on the road to my house as to who would be the greatest. I was still greatly offended at my fellow apostles.

I suppose I should forgive them. I suppose I should extend mercy to them.

"Lord, how often shall my brother sin against me and I forgive him? Our custom is to forgive three times, but will seven times suffice?" I asked feeling quite proud of my generosity.

Jesus answered, "I do not say to you that seven times is sufficient, but seventy times seven would be more like it."

Everyone gasped, except for me. As usual, my impulsive nature got the best of me, and I blurted out, "What?! Are you saying that I am to forgive a person four hundred and ninety times?! I can't do that! No human being could be that merciful!"

Jesus responded, "Beloved, God multiplies His pardons to you; therefore, you should do the same for others who are no more deserving than you.

"For this reason the Kingdom of heaven may be compared to a certain king who wished to settle accounts with his slaves. As he called the slaves to come before his throne, there was brought in one who owed him ten thousand talents, which is equal to about ten million dollars in silver. Since the man did not have the means to repay, the king commanded him to be sold, along with his wife and children and all that he had, and repayment to be made.

"The slave fell down, prostrating himself before the king, saying, 'Have patience with me, and I will repay you everything!'

"And the king felt compassion for him, so he forgave his debt and released him. That slave hurried out from his presence and found a fellow slave who owed him one hundred denarii, which is about the wages of one-hundred work days. That slave seized the man and choked him, saying, 'Pay back what you owe me!'

"His fellow slave fell down and pleaded with him, saying, 'Have patience with me, and I will repay you.'

"However, he was unwilling to forgive. Instead, he had him thrown in prison until he should pay back what was owed.

"His fellow slaves saw what the man had done, they were deeply grieved. They went to the king and reported what had happened.

"The king summoned the slave and said to him, 'You wicked slave, I forgave you all that debt because you entreated me. Should you not also have had mercy on your fellow slave, even as I had mercy on you?'

"And the king, moved with anger, handed him over to the torturers until he should repay all that was owed him."

That was one stupid man.

Jesus looked at each of us and shocked us all by saying, "So shall My heavenly Father also do to you, if you do not forgive your brother from your heart."[125]

"Seventy times seven," I whispered to myself, "how is that possible?"

CHAPTER TWENTY-SEVEN

L aban exclaims, "Peter, there are so many people I have not forgiven! I don't want Jesus to respond to me like that king responded to that man. I need help. I need to deal with these issues in my heart!"

Eleazer adds, "The same is true for me."

"But, Peter, what if I don't feel like forgiving?" Josiah asks.

"You don't have to feel like it, you just have to do it. Tell the Lord that you are willing to be willing. Ask for His help. Forgiveness is a choice; it is an act of your will. It is not an emotion, but a decision. Forgiveness is giving the person a gift that they may not deserve just as God has given you a gift that you don't deserve.

"Often, the emotion follows the decision, and many times you have to continually forgive the person until your heart is free and healed. I encourage you to ask the Lord to show you everyone you have unforgiveness towards, and then ask God to forgive you for not forgiving them. Once you've done that, tell God that you choose to forgive them. Ask the Father to bless them and heal your heart.

Forgiveness sets those you hold captive free, but it also sets you free. Unforgiveness is a cruel taskmaster and relentless in its goal of consuming you."

I wait as God silently moves on the hearts of these men, setting them free from their spiritual prison of unforgiveness.

After a short time, Eleazer exclaims, "The Lord is gracious to the extreme! I have never known anyone who is as forgiving and kind as He!"

I respond, "Jesus came to show us His Father. The parable of the king and his unworthy slave so clearly demonstrates the forgiving nature of God. He is indeed a Father who cares about His children. He is not willing that any should perish, but that all should come to repentance. He loves us and enjoys us. He responds to us with infinite lovingkindness just as that parable demonstrated. He is slow to anger, compassionate and abounding in lovingkindness. He is longsuffering and allows ample time for His children to repent, knowing that we are weak and like little children.

"I, for one, am thankful that God does not deal with us as our sins deserve, or we would all spend eternity separated from God in eternal punishment. He is faithful to grant mercy and forgiveness to all who ask."[126]

Laban replies, "In his desperate hour of need, that slave was shown extravagant mercy, but then he went out from the presence of the king and found a fellow slave who sinned against him in a trivial manner. Grabbing the man by the throat, he demanded that he make amends or else he would have him put in prison or worse. That king was certainly just in declaring that he was a wicked servant in not having compassion on his fellow brother—especially since the king had forgiven him such a huge debt. The sad thing is that I have lived my life just like that."

Eleazer interjects, "This is certainly not how God was

portrayed to me. I believed God to be distant, unconcerned about me or my affairs and mostly angry. I believed that He was greatly displeased with me because of my inability to keep His Laws perfectly."

"He is not that way at all, my friend. He is for us and not against us. As we strive against sin and pursue an intimate relationship with Him, we capture His heart. And just as He has forgiven each of us so much, we should forgive our enemies, even those who have imprisoned us," I reply.

"You don't mean Nero? You don't mean Brutus and the guards who have found great pleasure in tormenting us, do you?" Josiah asks.

Before I can answer, Laban adds, "Surely, you do not mean that we must forgive these evil men! These men are the very enemies of God! He cannot expect us to forgive them!"

Eleazer quietly answers, "I think that is exactly what he means, my friends."

"That was exactly what Jesus meant by this parable. We must forgive *everyone* who has sinned against us. Otherwise, your Father in heaven will not forgive your trespasses. Our debt of sin is very great. Every one of us owed a debt which we could not pay just as Nero has a debt that he cannot pay. If God should deal with us according to what we deserve, we would all be condemned.

"Justice demands satisfaction, my friends; therefore, God sent the Treasure of heaven to the earth to satisfy our debts, to become the ransom price for you and me. Our Father is infinitely merciful and is very eager, out of pure compassion, to forgive the sins of those who humble themselves before Him. And when He does so, the crime and its penalty are wiped away, and the judgment is cancelled because His Son bore our sins on the cross and paid our debts.

"But, lest you get the wrong idea, let me clearly say that just because God is faithful and just to forgive us of our sins that does not mean that we can live our lives according to the desires of the flesh. We are to live according to righteousness, truth and holiness. Neither does the grace of God negate our responsibility to live holy, pure lives.

"We are to live as servants, esteeming others as greater than ourselves. We must pursue wholehearted devotion to the Son of God. We must not demand retribution from those who are indebted to us, but we should remember how God extended tender mercies to us and do the same for others. To not extend mercy to our enemies is wickedness; it is great wickedness indeed," I answer.

Laban replies, "You ask something of me that is impossible. I have forgiven all others, but I cannot forgive these animals they call guards. Why should I forgive such evil, wicked men as these?"

"I agree with Laban. I do not have the power nor the desire to forgive them, for hatred burns in my heart against them. Their actions justify my hatred," Josiah says.

"Oh, my friends and brothers! Listen to the words that are coming out of your hearts! Should not those who have received mercy show mercy? Do you want to be like the man in the parable who was forgiven for the atrocities he committed but refused to extend the same kindness that was granted to him? We must show compassion toward our brothers in the same way as God did to us! Jesus did that for us. He did not wait until we came to our senses, but while we were yet sinners, He died for us," I respond.[127]

"I do not want to be like that unforgiving man, but I do not have any love in my heart for my captors. How can I forgive those for whom I feel only animosity?" Laban asks.

"Remember, forgiveness isn't a feeling; it is a choice. It is an act of your will. You must make the decision to forgive, to give them a gift they don't deserve. Jesus has had many opportunities to be offended with you, and yet He chose love every time!

"Sometimes it takes forgiving the person on a daily basis, and as you do, you will find your heart softening towards them. And the day will finally come when you realize that the forgiveness you chose to walk in has driven out the resentment and healed the pain that you once felt. God will help you as you ask Him for the grace to forgive and for the grace to love your enemies. I am living proof of that," I respond.

"I don't have much time for God to work this in my heart, Peter. It's not like I'm going to live for months or even weeks. I may not even live one more day. Therefore, I am not going to waste anymore time. I am going to ask God to help me forgive and even love Nero, Brutus and the other guards," Eleazer states.

"If Eleazer is willing to do this, then who am I to refuse?" Josiah states.

"Count me in, too," Laban adds.

I silently rejoice as my three brothers pour out their hearts before our Father of mercy and grace. And what a beautiful sound it is!

Once they grow quiet, I ask, "Shall I continue with the story, or do you need to rest?"

"Peter, we have no time to waste. Continue on," Eleazer answers.

CHAPTER TWENTY-EIGHT

After Jesus corrected my selfish view of forgiveness and deflated my obnoxious pride, John said, "Master, as we traveled here today, we saw a man we did not know casting out devils in Your name. We tried to stop him because he was not part of our group."

John may be tender, devoted and closely attached to Jesus, but he is just as ambitious as I am. There is more to his statement than meets the eye.

Jesus answered, "John, do not hinder him, for there is no one who shall perform a miracle in My name, and be able soon afterward to speak evil of Me."

What is He saying? I thought the twelve of us were His only chosen ones, His apostles, His authorized ambassadors! We were the ones Jesus sent to preach the news of the Kingdom and to heal the sick, delivering those in chains. How is it that others who are not one of us should be allowed the same rights and privileges?

In response to my unspoken thoughts, Jesus said, "He performed a miracle in My name, Peter. He is one of Mine. He who is not against us is for us. Whoever gives you a cup of water to drink because you are a follower of Christ, truly I say to you, he shall not lose his reward.

"Beware of making hasty conclusions based merely on external observations, My friends. There are many who love and follow Me who are not walking among us. Therefore, do not set yourself up as their judge.

"Be wise as a serpent and as harmless as a dove."[128]

CHAPTER TWENTY-NINE

Directing my attention back to my fellow prisoners, I say, "Jesus was clearly warning us against elitism. He knew the condition of our hearts and our desire to be seen as the 'man of the hour.' We were so quick to judge others based on external circumstances. The desire to be great causes a spiritual blindness, which is exactly what was happening with not only me, but also the other apostles."

Eleazer replies, "I certainly know what that is like."

I reply, "Many people live this way, my friend and brother. It is important for us as believers to pursue unity in the things that are essential to the gospel and extend liberty in the areas which are not essential to salvation, and in all things to respond in love. This was how Jesus lived His life."

"I can see so clearly the error of my ways and am so grateful to the Lord for rescuing me from my self-righteous pit," Eleazer responds.

Laban adds, "Eleazer, I too am guilty of judging others. I do it without even thinking. It is an automatic response and one that is often based on the clothes a man wears or the position he holds in society. I prided myself in the fact that I surrounded myself with only the best, most desirable people."

Josiah says, "Shhh, someone's coming!"

The opening and closing of doors makes me think that perhaps we're going to be fed. Our turn comes, and the door swings open with much creaking and groaning. Two guards stand in the dim light of the doorway. I squint in an effort to see who they are.

They must be new here; I have never seen them before.

Leaving the torch in the holder outside, they step inside with two buckets in hand. Holding a ladle to our mouths, they allow us to drink of the warm water. Having drank all I dare for fear of becoming sick, I say, "Greetings in the name of the Lord Jesus Christ who was crucified for you!"

"You must be one of those Christians," the younger of the two says.

"I am. And what of you, my friend? Have you met the Savior yet?"

"I did not even know that I had a Savior or that I needed one," he answers.

"If you have ever told a lie or cheated someone or had a wrong thought, then you need a Savior. So, tell me, what is your name, my friend?"

"I am Daniel, the son of John. And I have, on more than one occasion, told a lie. As a matter of fact, I am pretty good at lying and even better at getting away with it," he says laughing.

"I am Peter and would dare say that you most certainly need a Savior. But before I tell you more, I must ask what is the name of your friend?"

The other guard answers, "My name is Joab, and I have wanted to hear more about this Jesus for quite sometime, but first I would like to unchain your hands so that you can eat."

Carefully and as gently as possible, the two guards unlock the manacles around our wrists. They then hand us each a large piece of fresh bread.

They certainly aren't your typical Roman guards.

Closing the door Joab asks, "Peter, why do I need a Savior? I am a good man. I pride myself in being kind and reaching out to the hurting. I don't cheat, steal or lie. Tell me what this Savior can do for me?"

"You ask why you need a Savior—Joab, you need a Savior because of sin, for every human being has fallen short of the glory of God, except for One and His name is Jesus.

"And yes, Daniel, you may get away with lying here on this earth, but one day you will stand before your Creator and your God, and in that hour you will be desperate for an Advocate, my friend. Without Jesus as your Savior, you will spend eternity separated from God in eternal punishment."

"Who is this Advocate, and how does He help me?" Daniel asks.

"Let us say that you decide to accept the free gift of salvation, which washes your sins away and grants you entrance into the Kingdom of God. The day comes when you die and leave this world.

"To best explain how this Advocate can help you, allow me to use the language of an earthly courtroom. God sits on the throne as the King of everything. The prosecuting attorney is Satan, Jesus is your defense Attorney or your Advocate, and you are the accused.

"You stand before God's throne, guilty as accused, and dressed in filthy garments. This would be devastating for you if it were not for Jesus who stands by your side.

"Satan says to the Judge, 'Look at him! He stands here before You guilty and dressed in filthy garments! How dare he come before You in this manner—just look at this long list of sins that he has committed! This man deserves to be punished; he deserves to die!'

"God rebukes Satan saying, 'You're not his judge, and you have no right to pass judgment on My son! I have rescued him from your kingdom; therefore, your accusations have no grounds with Me. As for that long list of sins, they have been blotted out of My book.'

"He then opens a book titled, *The Lamb's Book of Life* and turns to a page with your name at the top; the page is completely covered with a very large blood stain. Every sin that you ever committed, every mistake, every wrong choice has been covered by the blood of Jesus who gave His life in order to save you from yourself.

"At this point, Jesus, who lives to intercede for you, steps between you and the throne saying, 'Father, I paid the price for his sins on the cross; You have already punished Me in his place.'[129]

"The King then turns to an angel standing nearby and says, 'Remove Daniel's filthy garments and place My robe of righteousness on him.'"

"The angel hastens to obey. Once you are dressed in robes of righteousness, God says to you, 'I have taken your iniquity away and have clothed you in festive robes.'[130]

"You, who were once guilty, now stand before the King of kings uncondemned and justified through faith in the Son of God! But this is only true if you accept Jesus' invitation to become a child of His Kingdom rather than a child of the kingdom of this world, which is what you are now.

"This is why you need a Savior. Without Him, you will be condemned to a fate worse than anything you could imagine. Without Him, Satan will have every legal right to condemn you, and you will be thrown out of the courtroom and sentenced to eternal punishment with Satan and his angels."

The Holy Spirit convicts Daniel and Joab. I can see the torment on their faces as they come to terms with the hopeless condition of their souls.

"Daniel, Joab, now is the day of salvation. Do not tarry, but surrender your lives to the living God who fashioned you in His image!" I plead.

Daniel cries out, "What must I do to be saved?"

"I am lost! I am in need! Tell me what to do!" Joab cries.

"Do you believe that Jesus Christ is the Son of God?"

"I do!" they cry in unison.

"Then repent, which means to turn away from your sins and your old way of life, and be baptized in the name of Jesus Christ for the forgiveness of your sins. And you shall receive the gift of the Holy Spirit, for this promise is for you and your children, and for all who are far off."[131]

"I will, I will turn from my wicked ways, but who will baptize us? You cannot, for you are in chains," Joab asks.

"Go to the guard, Malchus. Do you know him?"

"I do," Daniel answers.

"Good. Go to him and tell him your desire. He will baptize you and will welcome you into the church that meets in his home. You are now a part of the family of God, a citizen of His Kingdom; therefore, you should walk according to the ways of the King, following His example. It is important, as ambassadors of Christ, that you walk in a manner worthy of your calling, my fellow brothers."[132]

"We do not know the ways of our new King, so how will we know how to live in His Kingdom?" Daniel asks.

"Begin by walking in all humility and gentleness, with patience, showing forbearance to one another in love. Be diligent to walk in unity, in peace, for God loves unity in the midst of diversity.[133]

"Malchus will give you further instructions. Submit yourself to his leadership and those in the church. Take heart, my brothers, God is faithful to complete that which He has begun in you."[134]

Expressing their need to leave, they regretfully chain our hands back to the post. "We shall find Malchus even now, Peter," Joab states.

With his hand on the door handle, Joab adds, "Thank you for introducing Daniel and me to Jesus. I never knew—." His voice falters.

"I, too, thank you. Something too marvelous for words has happened within me this day, something that I never want to lose," Daniel says.

"I rejoice with you, for it was by the very hand of God that you came in here today," I respond.

"We bid you good-night," Joab says.

No sooner has the door shut than Eleazer says, "Peter, how is it that those two men were converted so easily? They barely know what they have given themselves to."

"Not everyone needs or requires as much persuasion as you, my brother," I answer, chuckling.

"I would guess that I was more difficult than most, but Peter, they haven't heard about Jesus' miracles or His life story. They don't really know Him."

"The gospel is very simple. Either Jesus is who He claimed to be or He is a fraud. The first step for anyone is to decide which you believe. Once you confess Jesus to be the Son of God, then you must humble yourself and follow Him allowing Him to become the One who makes the decisions for your life. He begins to stretch you and challenge your old habits and wrong motives. He brings you to the place where you have to answer this question: Will you love Him without stipulation, without hesitation or reserve? Will you be faithful to Him?

"As for Daniel and Joab, like you, they will grow in the knowledge of who Jesus is. They are like newborn babies. You don't give a newborn a leg of lamb to chew on, do you?

Of course not, you give them milk until they are able to digest meat. Such are the ways of the Kingdom. Malchus will guard them and feed them and watch over their souls. He will tell them all about Jesus."

Laban cries out, "But Peter, you told them to repent and be baptized. I have not been baptized! I, too, want to be baptized, but how can I in this place?!"

"I was thinking the same thing, Peter. I, too, want to be baptized!" Josiah adds.

"Peter, I want it all! I want to do everything that Jesus said for me to do. I desire the fullness of all that Jesus paid for on that cruel cross," Eleazer exclaims.

"The Lord understands that it is impossible for you to be baptized in water, my brothers. He does not condemn you for something that is beyond your ability to do."

"Oh, the agony of this prison!" Eleazer cries out.

"Oh, the torture of not possessing our freedom!" Laban exclaims.

"Oh, the pain of reaping the fruit of our sinful actions," Josiah adds.

"Take heart, my brothers, there is another baptism that you should know about. I should have already told you of it. There is no excuse for my not having done so, for it is crucial in the life of every believer. This baptism that I speak of is a filling, an indwelling of the Holy Spirit, which empowers you to walk in the manner that Jesus walked. Tell me, would you like this free gift from the Father?"

"We desire all that God has for us, Peter! Hold nothing back, but reveal all!" Eleazer exclaims.

"This is my desire as well," Laban says.

"As is it mine," Josiah states.

"What must we do to receive this baptism of the Spirit of God?" Eleazer asks.

"You simply ask for it," I answer.

"We just ask, and He will fill us?" Laban asks.

"Eleazer, suppose one of your sons asked you for a fish, would you give him a snake?"

"Of course not!"

"What about you, Laban. If your son asked you for bread, would you give him a stone?"

"I don't have a son, but if I did, I would never answer his request in such a heartless manner, even when I was in my unsaved state."

"If you then, being evil, know how to give good gifts to your children, how much more shall your heavenly Father give the Holy Spirit to those who ask Him?"[135]

"I will ask then," Eleazer states.

I wait. In a matter of minutes, all three of them are speaking in a new tongue.[136]

Eleazer says, "This is amazing! I feel so good!"

"For the first time in months, I feel no pain," Laban exclaims.

"I feel as though I have had too much wine," Josiah says.

"The Holy Spirit is better than wine, better than fine wine!" Eleazer exuberantly announces.

I respond, "This is the very thing that John the baptizer spoke about when he said, 'I baptize you with water, but Jesus will baptize you in the Holy Spirit.'[137]

"You see, my brothers, there is a Wine that comes from heaven that invigorates the spirit and empowers us to live a holy life. This Wine is so much better than the finest of earthly wines. Paul commanded the church in Corinth to be filled with the Holy Spirit rather than being drunk with wine. Jesus left earth so that His Father could send the Holy Spirit to us."

Eleazer exclaims, "What a wonderful gift! What a glorious gift! I have never known such love, such joy! In my lifetime, I have known much wine, but nothing compares to the filling up of my soul with the glorious

Spirit of God!"

I respond, "Drink, imbibe deeply, my friends. Allow the Holy Spirit to take possession of you. Allow His love to flood your very being and wash away your yesterdays. Allow Him to flow through every part of you and set you free from those things that hinder love.

"He loves you! He died for you! He cares about every detail of your life! He is a God who is near. He lives within you. His thoughts toward you are greater than the number of grains of sand in the earth. His love is higher than the heavens and deeper than the deepest ocean. His mercy never ends. God is good through and through.

"Enjoy the free gift of God, my friends. Enjoy all that He has for you!"[138]

CHAPTER THIRTY

Because the Jewish leaders were seeking to kill Jesus, He remained in Galilee, refusing to walk in Judea. With Jesus by my side, six months passed quickly.

It was September, 32 A.D., and the Feast of Tabernacles was just over a month away. All Jewish adult males were required to make the journey to Jerusalem to celebrate this important Feast.

I was sitting under a rather large tree when Jesus' brothers came looking for Him. I pointed them to a patch of trees just a stone's throw away where Jesus lay prostrate on the ground with His prayer shawl covering His head.

I wonder what business they have with Him on this fine day. It is common knowledge that Jesus' brothers do not believe that He is the Messiah.

Curious, I jumped to my feet and followed. His brothers stood around Jesus like a hungry pack of wolves. After silently making fun of Him, James cleared his throat. Jesus immediately looked up and warmly greeted His brothers.

As they exchanged pleasantries, I noticed something different about Jesus' countenance.

What is it?

I stepped closer, drawn by some inner need to know what it was that I was seeing. Jesus sat up; His tattered and tear-stained prayer shawl fell across His shoulders.

He invited His brothers to join Him on the thick carpet of grass, but they chose to remain standing.

Jesus appears to be pained, but why? What is it that fills His eyes with such a look of sorrow?

James said, "You know that the Feast of Tabernacles is at hand. Why is it that you have not made the necessary preparations to attend?"

Before He could answer, James continued, "Leave this remote place and return to Judea so that your disciples may see the works that you are doing. What point is there in doing works that only a few can see? And what point is there in doing works in remote places, in a house or in front of ignorant peasants?

"If you are the Messiah, as you claim to be, then do the things that a Messiah should do before the eyes of those in Jerusalem, in front of the Scribes and Pharisees. Or do your miracles at one of our feasts, in front of the multitude in Jerusalem. No one does anything in secret if he seeks to be known publicly. If you truly are able to do these things, then show yourself to the world!"

They certainly know that the Jews are seeking to kill Jesus. Why are they telling Him to go to Jerusalem? I would tell them exactly where they could go, if I was Jesus.

Jesus answered with amazing kindness, "My time is not yet here, but your time is always opportune. The world cannot hate you, but it hates Me because I testify to it that its deeds are evil."

"Why don't you speak in plain Hebrew?" James asked.

Jesus' brothers silently ridiculed Him as they glanced at each other.

Jesus chose to ignore their attitude and responded,

"You are free to go. Go to the Feast, but I will not yet go because My time has not yet fully come."

Shaking their heads and muttering among themselves, they slightly bowed.

They mock Him!

Jesus looked directly at me. I could see the caution in His eyes. I withdrew my silent accusations but felt great offense in my heart.

Jesus stood to embrace His brothers, but they turned away. Feeling the sting of their rude behavior, I hurried to His side and embraced Him. With His arm around my shoulder, He watched them walk away. Once they were well out of sight, He said, "Peter, one must never pick up the offense of another. It is important that you always walk in love, in compassion and in truth, My friend."

"But what they did was wrong, and I wanted them to know it," I responded.

"Simon, there is something much better than being right, something much better than getting even and that is being free!"

"But, Jesus they are so arrogant! Who do they think they are to treat you like this? It's even more insulting since they are Your brothers!"

"Peter, everyone is mistreated, abused, rejected and misunderstood in this life, but the redeemed have the opportunity to benefit from such suffering, if they will respond correctly to it," He answered.

"I do not understand how suffering can benefit anyone."

"The test of suffering separates the wheat from the chaff and reveals the hidden issues of the heart such as pride, anger and jealousy. When you encounter various trials, and you will, consider it all joy because the testing of your faith produces endurance. And endurance produces perseverance. And perseverance produces a vessel that is mature and complete and lacks nothing.[139]

"But, Jesus, they are Your brothers."

"Just because they are my brothers does not exempt them from wounding me, and neither does it give Me the right to retaliate.

"Simon, they have no understanding. They do not yet know who I am. But, the day will come when they will know and believe.

"We must love even those who rise up against us. Resist the urge to judge those who rise up against you. Instead, direct your energy towards loving them and pray for them because this is the highest way," He answered.

"Jesus, it would be easier for me to single-handedly conquer the entire Roman army than it would be for me to do what You ask. I know my heart, and it is extremely selfish and bent on having its own way and I do not possess the power to transform it."

"You don't, but I do," He stated matter-of-factly.

"Is it really possible?"

"Not only is it possible, but it is My intention. Peter, I lovingly pursue and completely transform those who allow Me to do so. A heart won through tenderness will be loyal and true. But, a heart won through force becomes a slave, and I am not looking for slaves. Therefore, I pursue you with lovingkindness and merely ask you to voluntarily return that love."

"At least slaves are obedient," I respond under my breath.

"Simon, I have myriads and myriads of angels at My beckon call to do whatever I desire; I do not need anymore slaves. What I do desire are friends, lovers, sons and daughters. I long for your friendship, Peter. I am not so much concerned about you 'getting it right,' because I know that if I can win your affections, then you will obey Me, and you will do so voluntarily not because you are forced to do so. "

Picking up a dry twig, He continues, "I give life to the dead places, Peter. My love will always be greater than your weakness."

"Oh, Jesus, how I long for that to be true!"

"Will you dare to believe, Peter? Will you dare to believe that My love is greater than your weakness, that My love is enough to carry you through?"

He waits for my answer as I wrestle with my doubts and fears. Clearing my throat, I finally answered, "I will try my best, Lord, I will."

"Good, that is all I need, Peter. Now, let us return to the others."

The following day, the men in all of the surrounding villages set out for Jerusalem, but we remained in Galilee with Jesus. The Feast was just over a month away, but many people were leaving early in order to hear the teachings of the rabbis.[140]

With all of the men journeying to Jerusalem, the numbers that followed Jesus were considerably less, which allowed us to travel in relative obscurity.

As He led us south through Galilee, I watched Him closely. He was quieter than normal, but He never failed to reach out to those we came in contact with.

After several days, my curiosity got the best of me and I asked, "Where are we going?"

"I have set My face to go to Jerusalem by way of Samaria."

What?! Not only is He going to Jerusalem, but He is going through Samaria! I know that this is the shortest route, but a route that is strictly avoided by Jews. We would rather take the long way around Samaria than to defile ourselves by going through it.

"By way of Samaria?" I asked, quite appalled at the thought.

"Yes, Peter, by way of Samaria," He answered.

He then turned His attention to a child hiding behind a bush quite a distance away. Calling to the boy, He said, "Your leprosy is cleansed!"

With a shout, the boy ran out of his hiding place shouting and praising the God of Abraham, Isaac and Jacob.

Being defiled by the Samaritans is awful, but I am more concerned about Jesus being in Jerusalem among the Pharisees who hate Him.

With each passing day, I grew more concerned for His safety. Finally, I asked, "Are we really going to the Feast?"

"Simon, whoever does not carry his cross and does not follow in My steps cannot be My disciple. He who has found his life shall lose it, and he who has lost his life for My sake shall find it."[141]

Carry my own cross! The cross is the most despised and shameful thing there is! What is He talking about? I was merely asking if we were going to Jerusalem.

We walked on in silence.

It was the close of the day when the first Samaritan village came into sight. Jesus sent two messengers on ahead in order to make arrangements for us to spend the night there.

Finding a large, flat rock, Jesus climbed up and sat down to rest. Inviting us to join Him, we sat at His feet, expecting Him to instruct us, but He merely closed His eyes and quietly worshipped the God of heaven. We eagerly joined in. John pulled out his flute while the rest of us sang and danced and clapped even though we were tired. Jesus soon joined the dance. We were quite a sight on the top of that rock dancing for joy, worshipping the God of heaven in a godless country like Samaria.

There is something within a Jewish heart that cannot help but dance anytime there is worship. Perhaps, it goes back to king David and his life of extravagant worship.[142]

We were still celebrating when the messengers returned with their heads bowed in shame. Jesus stopped dancing and said, "Yes?"

"Master, we did as You instructed, but when the Samaritans heard that You were traveling to Jerusalem for the Feast, they refused to offer You either lodging or hospitality."

This is not only bad manners, but also an open display of hostility towards Israel and a personal assault towards us.

Before Jesus could respond, James stomped his foot and said, "Just who do they think they are?"

John added, "How dare they refuse You this common courtesy! Just who do they think they are?!"

The two sons of thunder, James and John, with fire in their eyes and unbridled zeal for their Teacher, locked arms. John, with fist raised, continued, "Lord, do You want us to command fire to come down from heaven and consume them?"

James added, "Yeah, fire would be good!"

I chuckled. This was what Elijah did to the messengers of the evil and idolatrous king of Samaria. I thought back to our recent visit from Elijah and Moses, and my heart rejoiced at their response. I quickly made my way to their side eager to join in the fight should there be one.

A little fire might be exactly what is needed here. After all, one need only take a good look at these Samaritans to feel justified with such action, for they are a race of heathen Assyrians, whose very presence in Israel is humiliating. In the days of Nehemiah, their forefathers were our bitter enemies as they fought against the rebuilding of Jerusalem's walls, instead of aiding us as neighbors should.

In addition to the sins of their fathers, the condition of the present-day Samaritans is no better. They reject all of the Old Testament scriptures except for the five books of

Moses. *They worship at the ruins of the temple at Gerizim, which their fathers built in contempt of the true temple of God in the holy city, Jerusalem. And now they refuse us hospitality just because we believe the temple in Jerusalem is the only place to worship!*

Unconcerned with my opinions and not asking my advice, Jesus leaned forward and rebuked James and John, saying, "You do not know what kind of spirit you are of. The Son of Man did not come to destroy men's lives but to save them."

The depth of His love and compassion never ceases to amaze me. He really cares about them even though they are Samaritans and have rejected Him! Is there no end to His mercy?

I looked at James and John. Their zeal was admirable, and yet I could see that it was not pure. The fuel that fed there zeal was hatred for the Samaritans mixed with their devotion to Jesus, as well as some plain old carnal energy.

They aren't called the sons of thunder for no reason.

Jesus continued, "Do you not yet understand that I have come for all men, and that includes both Jew and Gentile? You, My friends, were chosen to live and proclaim a message of mercy to even the chiefest of sinners, to overcome evil with good and to call both Jew and Gentile, which includes Samaritans, into the Kingdom of heaven."

James and John hung their heads. Wasting no time, Jesus jumped from the rock and put His arm around their shoulders saying, "Come, My friends, let us go from here."

Why did Jesus choose to go to Jerusalem through Samaria anyway? Jewish men always take the roundabout way to Jerusalem by crossing to the east of the Jordan. It may be longer, but it certainly is more pleasant, for the Samaritans hate us, and the feeling is mutual.

If I were Jesus, I would march right into that village and make sure they understood just who they were turning away!

Once Jesus is crowned king of Israel, they will certainly be sorry for their behavior on this fateful day. I can hardly wait for that day!

We left the uncrowded roads of Samaria and returned to Jewish territory. Stopping at the first village, we were graciously received, rightfully so. After feeding us, they led us to the rooftop where we quickly spread out our pallets. Within minutes, I was fast asleep.

The morning sun rose way too soon. Jesus had already risen and was on His knees, His face lifted to heaven.[143]

What kind of fire burns within His soul that He can tarry for hours in prayer? And how is it that He denies Himself the common comforts and necessary sleep due a man?

From that day on, Jesus set His face toward Jerusalem with fierce determination and a great eagerness in His step.

Whatever awaits Him in Jerusalem certainly has captured His heart. I sure do hope it does not involve the Scribes and Pharisees.

As we traveled, the crowd grew larger, and Jesus healed all their sick.

We were on the dusty road to Decapolis when a man from the crowd, a Scribe, stepped in front of Jesus and said, "I will follow You wherever You go."

Why is this Scribe here? He should be in Jerusalem preparing for the Feast.

Jesus responded to him saying, "The foxes have holes, and the birds of the air have nests, but the Son of Man has nowhere to lay His head."

Jesus then turned to a man who stood by the side of the road and said, "Come and follow Me."

The man answered, "Lord, permit me first to go and bury my father."

Nothing is considered more sacred than burying the dead.

Jesus replied, "Allow the dead to bury their own dead; but as for you, go and proclaim everywhere the Kingdom of God."

The man's face displayed his shock and surprise.

Suddenly, another man pushed his way through the crowd shouting, "I will follow You, Lord, but first permit me to say good-bye to those at home."

Placing His hand on the man's shoulder, Jesus replied, "No one after putting his hand to the plow and looking back, is fit for the Kingdom of God."[144]

The man looked away.

Jesus certainly makes it clear as to what He requires of a follower of His.

As Jesus resumed His journey, I caught up with Him and said, "Why did You not allow that man to bury his father?"

"Simon Peter, to be a follower of Mine, you must embrace self-denial and wholehearted affection. The decision to follow Me is a decision to die to self."

"But he only wanted to bury his father," I said.

"Peter, there was so much more behind his request than that."

"There was?"

"Peter, I desire faithful followers. Let me ask you this: If your wife was faithful to you ninety-five percent of the time, but was unfaithful the other five percent of the time, you would not call her faithful, would you? Of course not. She would be considered unfaithful. The same is true in My Kingdom. Giving only part of your life to Me is not surrender, neither is it faithfulness. Either you are Mine, or you are not. Faithfulness means pursuing undivided affection. That does not mean that you will be perfect, but it does means that you will desire and pursue holiness."

"What you require is too difficult."

"Peter, is it too much for a husband to expect his wife to be completely faithful? To have no other lovers? To be true in every way and fully committed to their relationship?"

He waited for my answer.

"No, Lord, that is not too much too ask," I responded.

"Then why should I be satisfied with any less?"

"I understand," I replied.

"Peter, no one can serve two masters, for either he will hate the one and love the other, or he will hold to one and despise the other."[145]

"You require much, Lord."

"Peter, like a faithful, kind husband, I require all but demand nothing," He responded.

His words had given me much to think about.

After several days of arduous travel, we came into the region east of the Jordan called Peraea.

As we passed by the site where John baptized, Jesus stopped. I could not help but think of my old friend and his fierce faithfulness. I turned to Jesus; His face reflected the emotion within. I hurried to His side.

Jesus said, "Surely, there was none greater than John."

I responded, "This is the very place Your ministry began. This is where You were baptized and the dove rested on You and the heavens spoke."

His all-seeing eyes scanned the distant horizon. Turning His gaze back to me, He answered. "This is not really where it all began, Peter. You see, My friend, it all began in a place far, far from here, in a place far beyond the reach of humanity. It all began in the heart of God before time existed."

"What do You mean?" I asked.

Staring off into the distance, He answered, "In the beginning was the Word, and the Word was with God, and the word was God. He was in the beginning with God."

A Presence unlike anything I have ever felt swirled around me like a mighty rushing wind. I fell to my knees.

Jesus continued, "All things came into being by Him,

and apart from Him nothing came into being that has come into being. In Him was life, and the life was the light of men. The light shines in the darkness, but the darkness does not comprehend it."

My whole being trembled violently at His words.

Who is this Man? Who is this King of glory?

"He is the light. He came into the world, but the world does not know Him. He came to His own, and those who were His own did not receive Him. But as many as receive Him, to them He will give the right to become children of God, even to those who believe in His name, who were born of God."

"The Word became flesh and dwelt among men and they beheld His glory. John the baptizer bore witness of Him saying, 'He is the One who existed before me; therefore, He has a higher rank than I.'"

"Jesus, I thought I knew You, but I do not know You!" I cried out.

"I am the only begotten of the Father, full of grace and truth."[146]

"You are greater than the sons of men! You are brighter than the sun! You are higher than the highest mountain! You are purer than the waters flowing from Lebanon! You are beyond description!" I cry out in adoration.

Jesus looked at me with such devotion that I cried out, "Turn away from me, for I am a sinful man!"

"Peter, do not turn Me away when you come face to face with your weakness, but run to Me. Come Peter, for you delight My heart," He responds.

I stand on trembling legs.

"We will stay in this place for a while," Jesus said.

I was unable to respond.

During our sojourn there, Jesus did not withdraw in isolation, but spent His days healing the sick and teaching the people. Great multitudes followed Him wherever He went.[147] As for me, I came to love Him more every day.

CHAPTER THIRTY-ONE

I stop to pray, for the sound of approaching guards grows louder. The door creaks open, and I shield my eyes. The guard enters holding a small oil lamp and saying, "Have no fear, my friends."

Relief floods me as I recognize Joab's voice.

"Joab and I have brought something for you all of you," Daniel adds.

The two guards stand before us, grinning from ear to ear. Joab holds a small basket, and Daniel holds a bulging wineskin.

Wasting no time, they quickly unlock the chains around our wrists. Joab says, "Peter, we have brought the fruit of the vine and bread that we might celebrate the Lord's Supper together."

Daniel adds, "We tried to come sooner but was unable. The moment the other guards left, we came, eager to share this very special Supper with you."

Tears well up in my eyes. Eleazer is the first to speak, "Tell us what this Supper is that you speak of."

I answer, "On the night Jesus was betrayed, He took

unleavened bread and broke it saying, 'This is My body; eat it.'

"He then took a cup and gave thanks. He handed it to us saying, 'Drink from it all of you, for this is My blood of the covenant, which is poured out for many for forgiveness of sins.'

"Ever since that day, we eat the bread and drink the cup in remembrance of Jesus' death until He comes again. So, my friends, because of Daniel and Joab's thoughtfulness, we have the honor and privilege of observing this wonderful feast together. A feast that I have missed greatly."[148]

"Oh, how great! Oh, how glorious! What a beautiful deed this is that you have done!" Eleazer says to Daniel and Joab.

"I am overwhelmed by your kindness to us," Josiah says.

"And I am ever so grateful to have the privilege of partaking in the Lord's supper," Laban exclaims.

Like little children who are about to have their very first birthday party, my fellow prisoners excitedly rub their hands together in anticipation.

Daniel and Joab are just as excited as we are. We ever so quietly lift our voices in worship and adoration. With great joy and even tears, we eat the bread and drink the cup, celebrating the death and resurrection of our beloved Savior and King.

"What a glorious day!" I exclaim as quietly as possible.

"Actually, it's night," Daniel responds.

It takes a moment for his words to sink in, and then we all start laughing. We laugh until we are thoroughly exhausted.

Joab says, "We must leave before we are found out."

"Thank you, for your priceless gift, which ranks second only to the day I was accepted into the family of God,"

Simon Peter and the King

Eleazer says.

"I, too, thank you for making it possible for us to celebrate the Lord's death in this manner. I am eternally grateful," Josiah adds.

"Thank you again for thinking of us," Laban says.

Joab responds, "After our water baptism, Malchus prayed for us to be baptized in the Holy Spirit, and then he served us our first communion. It was so powerful. On our way home, Daniel and I started talking about how wonderful it would be for you to be able to eat of the Lord's Supper. We decided, at the first opportunity, we would bring the bread and the wine to you that we might celebrate together."[149]

Daniel adds, "How could we not do this for you when it was within our power? After all, we are now family and fellow heirs of an eternal Kingdom."[150]

"Thank you," I say.

"Oh, how grateful I am to you both!" Eleazer adds.

They quickly and regrettably chain us back to our posts. The door closes behind them, and Eleazer says, "I have to say that I have never felt what I feel right now. It is as if it there is a new joy in the very core of my being."

"It is unlike earthly joy, which comes from without," Laban adds.

"Life in the Kingdom of God is a strange thing," Eleazer comments.

"It is unlike any kingdom I have ever heard of," Josiah states.

"The Kingdom of heaven is an inside-out, upside-down Kingdom," I say.

"Indeed?" Eleazer says, asking for more information.

"This Kingdom is the only kingdom I know of where its subjects must lose in order to gain and must die in order to live," I say.[151]

Our door opens again, and Joab enters with a stranger

265

in tow. "Look what I found outside your door," he whispers.

Joab gently places the man in front of me saying, "This is Eli. He is a slave. He had his ear plastered against the door, listening to our conversation. He wonders if salvation is possible for slaves. I told him that you would know the answer to that question, Peter. And while you do so, I need to step out for a moment."

Joy surges through me at the thought of a hungry soul searching for God. "Oh, my friend, Jesus came to seek and save the lost regardless of their social status or race. Yes, you can enter into the family of God, into His Kingdom. That is the beauty of our Father; He is no respecter of persons.[152] He does not wish for any to perish, but His great desire is for all to turn from their evil and selfish ways to a God who delights in helping them.[153]

"You can know Him, my friend. Is that what you desire?"

With his head bowed low, this man dressed in rags answers, "Many months ago, I heard that a Messiah had been sent from heaven to save mankind. I have searched long and hard for Him but to no avail. Several days ago, I overheard Daniel and Joab talking about this Messiah. When I saw them today, I followed them here to your door and dared to listen."

"Today is the day of salvation for you, my friend," I state.

I turn to Eleazer and say, "My friend, you expressed a desire and prayed for an opportunity to share the gospel with someone. Well, here's your chance. Why don't you tell Eli about your newly found Savior, Jesus?"

"I would love to!" He responds with great enthusiasm.

After Eleazer takes Eli on a journey through Jesus' life, Eli confesses his belief in Jesus as the Son of God, the Messiah sent from heaven to save the world. Eleazer then leads him in a prayer where he surrenders his life to his King and accepts His forgiveness.

Joab returns grinning broadly. He says, "I found Malchus and told him about Eli. He has instructed us to bring him to his house so he can be baptized."

Eli asks, "What is baptism?"

"Baptism is a symbolic act of having your sins washed away, of being buried with Jesus in the watery grave and rising again to a brand new life. It is like being born again," I answer.

Eli responds, "Then, do not hold back! Baptize me and wash away my sins!"[154]

Daniel says, "After Joab was baptized, he looked up at me and said, 'That's the best bath I've ever had, and I didn't even use soap.'"

We all laugh.

Calling Eli to my side, I lay my hand on him, and he is filled with the Holy Spirit and begins speaking in tongues and prophesying.[155]

It is all we can do to restrain ourselves from shouting. For the first time, Eli dares to look into the eyes of another man and says, "I have finally found the One who loves me! I am finally free!"

Joab says, "I hate to be the one who breaks up this celebration, but we must go before morning comes and the other guards return."

"God bless you as you spread the good news," I say as they quickly leave.

"This has been quite a day," Eleazer remarks.

"It makes it worth it, does it not?" Laban asks.

"It most certainly does," Eleazer answers.

"Peter, what about this baptism that you spoke of? We cannot be baptized, so what about us?" Josiah asks.

"God knows that, my friend. He sees your heart and He will not penalize you for something that is beyond your ability to do," I answer.

With great joy and peace flooding my soul, I fall asleep,

but it is short lived. Shouting fills our cell as our prison door is suddenly flung open. Trying to avoid the sharp pain from the light from their torches, I cover my eyes with my forearm. Over the sound of cursing and shouting, I can hear chains being unlocked.

Who is it? Who have they come for?

I try once again to see but find that the light is just too bright; my eyes cannot endure it. I call out, but the only response I receive is a sudden blow across the back of my head, causing my face to crash into the post. I fight to remain conscious as blood pours out of my nose and mouth.

"Oh, God help! Whoever they have come for, be with them and strengthen them!" I cry out.

"Stop your praying!" an angry voice shouts.

My head is spinning. In the distance, I hear Eleazer's voice but cannot understand what he is saying.

"Eleazer, what are you saying?" I ask, choking on the blood running down my throat.

"I told you to shut-up!" the voice shouts.

A foot lands in the middle of my back, which causes me to vomit violently. While gasping for air, one of my friends is dragged past me. Fighting desperately to lift my head that I might see who it is, I cry out, "Remember the Lord, my friend, remember the Lord!"

Once more, a blow is delivered to the back of my head.

"Who are you taking?" I ask just before I pass out.

To be continued....

For this perishable must put on the imperishable,
and this mortal must put on immortality.

When this perishable will have put on the imperishable,
and this mortal will have put on immortality,
then will come about the saying that is written,
'Death is swallowed up in victory.'

O death, where is your victory?
O death, where is your sting?[156]

A note from the Artist...

Again, Rhonda Calhoun has given me the privilege of painting a picture for one of her books. This is the second in a series on the life of Peter, the fisher of men.

There was a moment when Peter saw Truth. That is what I tried to paint. It seems easy for us who believe to say Who He is—especially on this side of the cross, but the disciples could not see until that moment and only Peter seems to have received the revelation, "You are the Christ, the Son of the living God."

In truth, though, each one of us must receive that same revelation in order to believe. He is the One who gives us the revelation—we choose to believe or not to believe.

I am overwhelmed at the ecstatic simplicity of the Lord's dealing with us through revelation. He reveals because He loves. He wants us. He wants me. He wants you. He wants us as His own thus He reveals Himself to us.

When we face the hardest of tests and trials of life and death, He will reveal Himself in a myriad of ways, but when we see Him as the Christ, the Son of the living God, we can and will face those tests and trials and become more than conquerors through Christ

271

who loves us.

To know Christ is to embrace the cross. It is because of the cross that we are saved, healed, set free from every bondage and know peace and joy in this life and beyond. Are these the keys of the Kingdom Jesus gave to the disciples and His church? Yes, yes and more, much more!

I pray" that the God of our Lord Jesus Christ, the Father of glory, may give to you the Spirit of wisdom and revelation in the knowledge of Him..."

Blessing in the name of the Lord,
Pam Macchi

ENDNOTES

CHAPTER ONE
1   Matthew 5:45; Proverbs 18:10; Psalm 91
2   Hebrews 12:2
3   I Corinthians 1:27-28
4   I Corinthians 2:14; John 3:8
5   Hebrews 7:25; Romans 8:2
6   Matthew 5:11-12

CHAPTER TWO
7   Matthew 12:38-45; Luke 11:14-36
8   Matthew 12:46-50; Mark 3:31-35; Luke 8:19-21

CHAPTER THREE
9   Psalm 139:8-12
10   II Corinthians 12:9

CHAPTER FOUR
11   Isaiah 6:9
12   Matthew 13:1-52; Mark 4:1-34; Luke 8:4-18; Joel 3:13
13   Romans 8:28
14   Matthew 5:20-30

15 Matthew 8:18, 23-27; Mark 4:35-41; Luke 8:22-25
16 Matthew 8:28-34; Mark 5:1-20; Luke 8:26-39

CHAPTER FIVE
17 Psalm 24:7-10
18 Psalm 27:4
19 Isaiah 53:3-6
20 Revelation 21:3-5
21 Song of Solomon 4: 7
22 Ephesians 5:25
23 John 16:7-15
24 Philippians 4:6-8
25 Hebrews 12:1-3
26 Revelation 3:11
27 Matthew 25:21
28 Hebrews 12:2

CHAPTER SIX
29 John 21:25
30 Luke 11:10
31 Matthew 11:29
32 Matthew 11:28-30
33 Matthew 9:18-26; Mark 5:21-43; Luke 8:40-56

CHAPTER SEVEN
34 Psalm 142:5-6
35 Psalm 23
36 James 5:13; I Peter 4:3
37 II Peter 3:9; Revelation 21:4
38 James 1:12; Revelation 2:10
39 Hebrews 13:8
40 Philippians 3:8-10
41 Romans 2:4

CHAPTER EIGHT
42 Matthew 9:27-31
43 James 4:6, 10
44 Philippians 2:3-4

45   Colossians 3:12; I Peter 5:5
46   Romans.2:4
47   John 16:33
48   Matthew 5:5; Philippians 2:3-9
49   James 4:6
50   Luke 18:27
51   Matthew 9:32-34
52   Matthew 13:53-58; Mark 6:1-6
53   Matthew 9:35-38

CHAPTER NINE
54   Acts 9:1-19
55   I Corinthians 4:10
56   II Peter 1:14
57   James 5:17,18
58   Galatians 522-23
59   Galatians 6:9
60   Matthew 7:7
61   Hebrews 11:1

CHAPTER TEN
62   I Corinthians 9:14
63   Matthew 10:1-42; 11:1; Mark 6:7-13

CHAPTER ELEVEN
64   Mark 6:12
65   John 18:36; II Timothy 4:18; James 2:5

CHAPTER TWELVE
66   Matthew14:1-12; Mark 6:14-34; Luke 9:7-11
67   Mark 6:30-34; Luke 9:10-11

CHAPTER THIRTEEN
68   II Corinthians 4:8-11
69   James 1:12
70   I Peter 1:13
71   I Peter 1:9
72   I Peter 1:22

CHAPTER TWENTY
99 Matthew 16:1-4; Mark 8:10-131
100 Matthew 5:20
101 Matthew 16:5-12; Mark 8:14-21
102 Mark 8:22-26
103 Matthew 16:13-20; Mark 8:27-30; Luke 9:18-21
104 Matthew 16:21-26; Mark 8:31-38; Mark 9:1;
    Luke 9:22-25
105 Matthew 16:27-28; Mark 9:1; Luke 9:26-27; James 1:9;
    Proverbs 24:12; I Peter 4:14-16
106 Galatians 2:20
107 Matthew 19:26; Luke 1:37

CHAPTER TWENTY-ONE
108 Zechariah 12:10

CHAPTER TWENTY-TWO
109 Psalm 103:1-11
110 Psalm 103:12-14
111 Psalm 103:11
112 Psalm 104:1-24
113 II Kings 2:1-15; Deuteronomy 34:5-7
114 Matthew 17:1-13; Mark 9:1-13; Luke 9:27-37

CHAPTER TWENTY-THREE
115 Hebrews 5:8
116 Ephesians 3:16-20

CHAPTER TWENTY-FOUR
117 Matthew 17:14-21; Mark 9:14-29; Luke 9:37-42
118 Matthew 17:22-23; Mark 9:30-32; Luke 9:43-45
119 Hebrews 10:4
120 James 1:17
121 Matthew 17:24-27; Ex. 30: 11-15

CHAPTER TWENTY-FIVE
122 Philippians 2:6

CHAPTER THIRTY-ONE
148 Matthew 26:26-29
149 Romans 6:3-4
150 James 2:5; Ephesians 3:6
151 Philippians 1:21
152 Acts 10:34
153 I Peter 3:9
154 Romans 6:1-7
155 Acts 19:1-6
156 I Corinthians 15:53-55

OTHER BOOKS BY THE AUTHOR

SIMON PETER AND THE MASTER by Rhonda Calhoun is the first book in a series. This book is the result of a dream where Rhonda saw Peter sitting in a Roman prison sharing the gospel with his fellow prisoners. This book paints a clear picture of what it was like to walk with the Master on the earth.

SIMON PETER AND THE KING by Rhonda Calhoun is the continuing story of Peter and his life with the Messiah, the King of kings. This story unveils the Carpenter from Nazareth and reveals that He is indeed the One promised by the prophets to take away the sins of the world. You will fall more in love with this Man from Israel as you walk with Him through the pages of this book.

THE BRIDE by Rhonda Calhoun is a fascinating and life-changing allegory based on the Song of Solomon. *The Bride'* is the story of a King pursuing the heart of a young shepherdess. The truth that God's love is greater than our weakness is clearly portrayed. The girl is won by a King who refuses to give up on her and reveals His glorious character and His infinite love to her. This book shows us how God views us and how He feels about you.

BLESSED ARE THE POOR by Rhonda Calhoun is a gripping collection of real-life stories from Danny and Rhonda's ministry with the poor and homeless of Kansas City. Each chapter is a portrait of a man, woman, or child who lives in drastic poverty and whose lives have impacted the author in profound ways. This book not only paints a picture of what it is like to live in poverty, sickness and hopelessness, but it also describes the supernatural ways God meets the needs of His children. He still multiplies bread. Even though their circumstances may seem impossible, in the midst of darkness, hope rises and love flows. Your heart will certainly be impacted and enlarged as you read these powerful testimonies of extravagant faith.

STUDY GUIDES

FATHER HEART OF GOD STUDY MANUAL is an excellent 100+ page study manual. Rhonda digs deep into the word of God revealing the Father's heart for those living in poverty. You will also discover how extravagant our Father is to all of His children regardless of their social status. After all, we all look the same at the foot of the cross.

THE BRIDE STUDY MANUAL can be used alone or with *The Bride'*. This in-depth study manual goes through the Song of Solomon verse by verse and phrase by phrase explaining, in easy to understand language, this highly symbolic book. The manual also includes a fascinating teaching on the Jewish betrothal customs during the time of Jesus. This manual is perfect for those who desire to dig deep into the bridal message. It is a great bible study tool for both individuals and groups.

KID'S EXPLOSION MANUAL explains how to organize a fun, bible-based outreach to children in your neighborhood, church, park, or inner city. Part One tells David's story and his first visit to one of our Kid's Explosion's, which gives you an insider's view of what the program looks like. Part Two is step-by-step instructions of how to start, organize and run your own outreach. The manual includes many helpful tools such as lists of games, memory verses, and bible stories.

TEACHING DVD'S AND CD'S:

SONG OF SOLOMON Join instructor Rhonda Calhoun as she explores the depths and heights of the Song of Solomon. Your life will be enriched and your heart ignited as you journey with her through this incredible story describing the infinite love the King has for us, His bride. Rhonda's insightful and delightful teaching explores the glorious truths found in each verse of this eight chapter Song. She lays a strong foundation for the bridal paradigm using numerous scriptures and also teaches the Jewish betrothal customs during Jesus' day, which clearly portrays our relationship with the Bridegroom King. Available in a 10-DVD set or 19-CD set.

JOURNEY THROUGH THE SONG OF SOLOMON is a gripping 80 minute overview of the Song of Solomon. Several times during this fascinating teaching, the Holy Spirit grips Rhonda's heart and she speaks prophetically. This is a very powerful message, which will move you to tears and fill your heart with hope as you see your true identity and experience the great delight that the Father feels for you, His eternal partner. (This is one of Rhonda's favorites.) (CD)

THE REAL CINDERELLA STORY is a teaching shared by Rhonda Calhoun. This fascinating teaching reveals the Bride of Christ and her Bridegroom as told through the Cinderella fairy tale. This heartwarming, eye-opening teaching will inspire and create a greater love in your heart for your Bridegroom King. Great for children from 10 to 90, male or female. (CD)

JOURNEY INTO THE PROPHETIC is an excellent two part teaching on the wonders, difficulties and delights of learning how to hear God's voice. It explores the nature and heart of God as a Father who absolutely loves to communicate with His children. A delightful message. (2-CD set)

JEWISH BETROTHAL CUSTOMS This eye-opening teaching explores the engagement customs during the time of Jesus and how they relate to us today. It paints a clear picture of the nature of the relationship that Jesus longs for. You will be amazed and challenged by the truths you will discover hidden in the Lord's Supper. A must for every believer. (CD)

WORSHIP CD'S:

ONE THING I DESIRE is an outstanding intercessory worship CD from the International House of Prayer in Kansas City. The worship songs and intercessory prayers are taken straight from the Song of Solomon and Psalms. The singers sing the scriptures in the form of prayer while others sing the Lord's response to their cries. This highly anointed worship CD will quickly become one of your favorites.

BETTER THAN LIFE by Julie Meyer is an excellent worship CD that was recorded at the International House of Prayer in Kansas City. Julie is an anointed and very gifted worship leader. This new CD brings the listener into the realization that we are lovely to God even in our weakest moments. Her worship songs will encourage your heart and lead you into the presence of God.

THE FATHER'S LOVE LETTER is a most powerful and heart touching CD by Father Heart Communications. The first 'song' is actually a powerful love letter from the Father based on the scriptures. The voice of a kind and loving father reads the love letter to you while anointed music plays in the background. The second is a reading of the scriptures that speak of how your Father feels about you. The third is a beautiful prayer in response to the Father's extravagant love. The fourth is a call to take the message of the Father to the broken and hurting. (Words by Barry Adams © 1999. Music: Robert Critchley © 2000 Wild Ox Publishing. Narration: Roy Lamont.)

OTHER RESOURCES:

SONG OF SOLOMON ANOINTING OIL. This delightfully fragrant oil is made from the eight spices listed in Song of Solomon 4:13-14. These spices represent intimacy with God and godly character. This oil comes in a one ounce roll-on bottle, which is easy to carry in pocket or purse.

NEW BEGINNINGS ANOINTING OIL. This wonderfully fragrant oil is made from the oils found in Isaiah 41:18-20. This oil symbolizes the changing of the seasons, the desert becoming a pool of water and the parched ground flowing with springs of water. This oil represents the truth that God promises to do the impossible in and through our lives. He promises to redeem, restore and make us fruitful that all might see His glory. Also in a one ounce roll-on bottle, which is easy to carry in pocket or purse.

PRODUCT ORDER FORM:

BOOKS:	QTY.	PRICE	TOTAL
SIMON PETER AND THE MASTER	____	$ 15.00	____
SIMON PETER AND THE KING	____	$ 15.00	____
THE BRIDE	____	$ 16.00	____
BLESSED ARE THE POOR	____	$ 10.00	____
THE BRIDE STUDY MANUAL	____	$ 20.00	____
THE FATHER HEART OF GOD STUDY MANUAL	____	$ 20.00	____
THE KID'S EXPLOSION MANUAL	____	$ 20.00	____

TEACHING DVD'S & CD's:

	QTY.	PRICE	TOTAL
THE SONG OF SOLOMON CLASS			
(10 DVD SET)	____	$110.00	____
(19 CD SET)	____	$110.00	____
JOURNEY THROUGH SONG OF SOLOMAN (CD)	____	$ 10.00	____
JOURNEY INTO THE PROPHETIC (2 CD SET)	____	$ 15.00	____
JEWISH BETROTHAL CUSTOMS (CD)	____	$ 10.00	____
THE REAL CINDERELLA STORY (CD)	____	$ 10.00	____

WORSHIP DVD'S

	QTY.	PRICE	TOTAL
ONE THING I DESIRE	____	$ 15.00	____
BETTER THAN LIFE	____	$ 15.00	____
THE FATHER'S LOVE LETTER	____	$ 13.00	____

ANOINTING OIL:

	QTY.	PRICE	TOTAL
SONG OF SOLOMON ANOINTING OIL	____	$ 10.00	____
NEW BEGINNINGS ANOINTING OIL	____	$ 10.00	____

SUBTOTAL $_____

Shipping, add 10% (minimum of $2.00) $_____

(U.S. funds only) **Total Enclosed** $_____

SEND PAYMENT WITH ORDER FORM TO:

Heart Publishing
12905 South 71 Hwy. #177
Grandview, MO 64030

Mailing address: (please print)

Name: _____

Street: _____

City _____ State _____ Zip _____

We Accept Master Card, Visa, or Discover:

Card Number: _____

Expiration Date: _____

V -Number: _____
(last 3 numbers on back of card on signature line)

Phone Number: _____

order from our on-line bookstore at:
www.harvesthome.org
or

For phone orders, bookstore orders
or quantity discounts call:

816-522-9011